ROSENBORG
PALACE

A GUIDE TO
THE CHRONOLOGICAL COLLECTION
OF THE DANISH KINGS

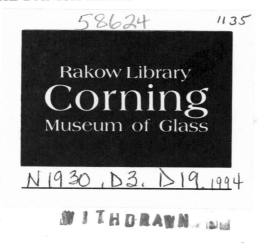

COPENHAGEN 1994
ROSENBORG
© 1994 by Rosenborg
3rd edition by Jørgen Hein and Peter Kristiansen
Drawings: Birte Skov, Maria Kristina Gottfries (p. 6)
Translation: Paula Hostrup-Jessen and Paulette Møller
Printed in Denmark by Poul Kristensen
Grafisk Virksomhed, Herning
ISBN 87-89542-20-7

Contents

Practical Information

The room numbers in this guide correspond to the numbers seen above the entrance door of each room. Only the most important exhibits are numbered. However, the catalogue of the Treasury and the Arms Collection is complete.

The History of the Palace

As the cramped town of Copenhagen with its heavy medieval castle was hardly the ideal residence for a young, ambitious Renaissance ruler, Christian IV preferred Frederiksborg Palace, built by his father, 35 km away. Even so, he planned many new buildings and an expansion of Copenhagen, the capital. East of the old town he acquired much property, where he founded in 1606 the park still called The King's Garden (Kongens Have).

Here, in 1606-07, he built a two-storey »summerhouse«, now the core of the south part of Rosenborg, with a spire-crowned stair turret facing the town and a bay to the east. As a result of hasty construction and faulty foundations, in the following year the stair turret had to be torn down and the building faced. Undismayed, Christian IV continued building. A new excavation shows that the foundations of the palace in its present length were laid. In 1610 the central part of the gatehouse was erected.

A new palace, twice the size of the original, was built in 1613-15. The present length was thus attained, but there were still only two storeys. There were two bays to the east and a stair turret on the central axis. The house was habitable from 1615, but construction continued from 1616-24. The storey containing the Long Hall was added, and the bays were converted to the existing spire-crowned towers. The Great Tower was built on the west side. In 1624 Christian IV first referred to his »great House in the Garden« as Rosenborg.

The design of the stair turret is not known, but the vital problem of a suitable link to the State Apart-

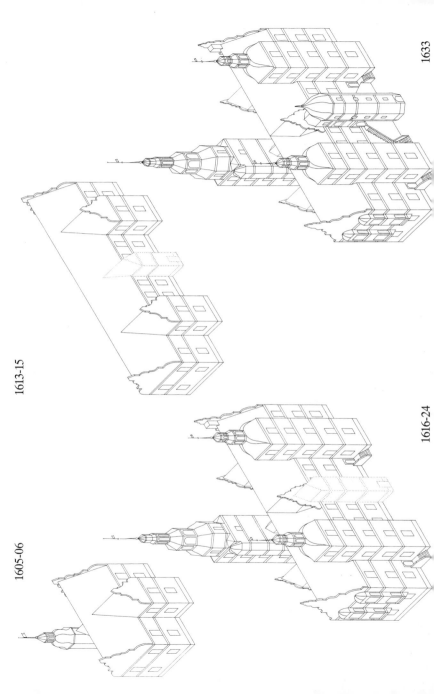

1613-15

1605-06

1633

1616-24

ments on the first and second storeys remained unsolved until the wedding of the eldest son in 1634. The stair turret was demolished and replaced by the present one and two exterior stairways extending from doors by the side towers up the facade to the openings, now glass-covered, in the structure connecting the palace and the tower, which contained the staircase to the top storey. These stairways were demolished in 1758, after which the stair turret was extended to the bottom.

Rosenborg, with its surrounding moat and drawbridge, was a playful version of a fortification. Today, with its high towers and red masonry with sandstone ornaments, it is a distinguished example of Christian IV's many building projects. The palace is built in the special Renaissance style which became typical of Danish buildings during this period, although it was originally inspired by the architecture of the Netherlands. The architects, Bertel Lange and Hans van Steenwinckel, worked on the palace, but there is no doubt that the basic idea was that of Christian IV.

The King's Residence

The Rosenborg interiors are excellently preserved because the palace has not been intensively used since 1710 – in the reign of Frederik IV, the great grandson of the builder, Christian IV. The original plan of the palace was as follows: the ground floor comprised the private apartments. In the north end was the Winter Room (Room 1), the King's Study (Room 2) and the Bedroom (Room 3). The south end contained the Queen's suite: the Great Chamber (Room 6), a small chamber, called the Jewellery Room (now closed), together with a bedroom, oriented across the house (Rooms 5 and 7). In the central area there was a transverse entrance hall flanked by a silver room in the stair turret, and in the Great Tower, the King's famous tin-lined bathroom with indoor plumbing.

In the entrance hall, a wooden staircase led to the first floor. The south end of this floor formed the Red Hall, which was the biggest room in the original summerhouse. In the centre there was a hall, and above the Winter Room was the King's Audience Chamber (Room 10), from which one could retire to »the Golden Chamber« (Room 9).

The room division in the upper storey is unaltered, although only the two Dutch fireplaces in the Long Hall (Room 21) are original.

In the reign of Frederik III several changes were made. On the ground floor, the King and the Queen exchanged apartments, and Sophie Amalie had one chamber (Room 3) lacquered in Chinese style after the latest fashion. The ceiling shows the Olympic gods surrounding the Queen as Hera, a symbol of divine approval of the absolute monarchy. The King had the Marble Room (Room 5) furnished in the same style. The walls are covered with marbled stucco, the Danish provincial coats-of-arms are seen on the walls and the richly embellished ceiling, and the ceiling paintings depict the regalia being brought from heaven. On the first floor, yet another room was furnished in the Chinese style (Room 9). It was completed in 1665 and is the oldest preserved room of its style in Europe. The Queen installed an »ascending chair« (a lift) as a private connection between this room and the room below (Room 2).

The major contribution of Christian V was a set of tapestries hung in the Long Hall (Room 21), but these were later moved to Christiansborg.

Frederik IV was more radical. The transverse hall was divided into the stone corridor (7) and the Dark Room (4), which Frederik IV furnished as a conjugal bedroom with silk wall-coverings and a mirrored fireplace. The bathroom became the Queen's boudoir (now closed off), to which a door to the garden at the west was later added.

The first storey was changed to its present floor plan. The Mirror Room (off Room 13) is the only original room from the time of Frederik IV. In the Long Hall (Room 21) he had the vaulted stucco ceiling built, with its motif of the Danish coat-of-arms, the Regalia, and the Orders of the Elephant and the Dannebrog, together with the important political events of his reign. The Glass Cabinet (Room 22) was furnished in 1714. But Rosenborg became too small for the splendour-loving King, who built other summer castles for himself. Thus it eventually became what it is today: a museum of the royal house. In the 18th century, the palace served various functions, but the royal family resided here on only two occasions, both emergencies: after the Christiansborg fire in 1794, and during the English attack on Copenhagen in 1801.

The Collections

Rosenborg is unique, above all for its long museum tradition. Already in the reign of Frederik III, the royal family's private treasures began to be housed here. The core of the collection consisted of riding trappings and parade arms from Christian IV's magnificent collections at Sparepenge, a small pavilion in the gardens of Frederiksborg Palace. Immediately preceding the Swedish occupation of Sealand in 1658, the treasures of Sparepenge were transferred to Rosenborg Palace, and in the 1660s the collections of heirlooms and »curiosities« as well as costumes followed. During the reign of Christian V, the Regalia Collection and other treasures from Copenhagen Castle were added, to be followed in the reign of Frederik IV by collections of glass and porcelain.

The new additions were housed in the tower rooms around the Long Hall: the Regalia Cabinet over which there were three armouries in the Great Tower; the Glass Cabinet in the north-east tower; and the

Throne Chamber, in which the furnishing of a Porcelain Cabinet was planned in the southeast tower. The locations were chosen for their proximity to the Long Hall, which became the preferred audience chamber of the newly founded Absolutism. Following the anointing of Christian V in 1671, the coronation chair of narwhal tusk, guarded by the three silver lions, was placed here. Later on, the Hall was modernised with tapestries and a new stucco ceiling. Rosenborg's upper storey thus became a display of the dignity and lineage of the royal family, an impressive sight which was allowed to remain even after the completion of the new residential palace, Christiansborg, in 1740. Subsequent additions comprised gold dinner services from the Royal Silver Room, a collection of mineral and shells, and in 1783, the Royal Collection of Coins and Medals, formally established as a museum.

Among Rosenborg's many collections, two have curious histories. The Costume Collection probably originated in Christian IV's desire to preserve his blood-stained clothing from the naval battle at Kolberger Heide. Later costumes were similarly connected with particular events and were therefore preserved – coronation and wedding robes, royal gifts etc. With few exceptions, only men's garments found their way to the Rosenborg collection.

The Crown Jewels were originally bequeathed for the use of the reigning Queen because »in this royal family there have been so few jewels, and no crown jewels at all«, as the benefactress, Queen Sophie Magdalene, wrote in her will. The jewels, supplemented with later gifts, are still used on State occasions.

The contents of the Royal Kunstkammer (Cabinet of Curiosities), situated at Christiansborg, were not of such a personal nature. The Kunstkammer was founded by Frederik III, who was thus the founder of Danish museums.

In the early 19th century, it was suggested that Rosenborg be opened to the public. To this end, A.W. Hauch, scientist and court official, drew up a plan in 1813, innovative in its exhibition technique, suggesting the replacement of the existing »theme« rooms with a chronological exhibition of the successive royal families. A walk round the museum would thus be a journey through the history of Denmark from Christian IV to the present day, for which reason at the time of its opening in 1838 a room for the reign of Frederik VI was arranged.

The collections were augmented with the closing of the Kunstkammer in 1824. The next important development occurred under the custodianship of J.J.A. Worsaae in the 1860s, with additions both from the royal palaces c. 1860 and from the Royal Museum of Art in Dronningens Tværgade, which was closed down in 1867.

In 1868 a room was furnished to the memory of Frederik VII, the last king of the House of Oldenborg. This was followed in 1910 by another for Christian IX, the first of the Glücksborg branch of the family, now part of the continuation of the Collection on exhibition at Christian VIII's Palace at Amalienborg and covering the period 1863-1947.

After the establishment of the Constitution and the abolition of Absolutism in 1849, the royal palaces became state property. In 1854 Frederik VII allowed the Rosenborg Collection to become entailed property passed on from king to king.

The Rooms: History, Function and Furnishings

Room 1. Christian IV's »Winter Room«

Of the palace's original rooms, the Winter Room, which was the most important of the King's private chambers, is the best preserved. The rich panelling was begun by court cabinet-maker Gregor Greuss and completed by others in 1620. The paintings inlaid in the panels, purchased in Antwerp, constitute a unique collection of Netherlandish art. Although most of the paintings are anonymous, some are ascribed to known artists such as Joos de Momper II, Pieter Snayers and Louis de Caullery. The ceiling, with Pieter Isaacsz' mythological paintings, including the Feast of the Gods and the Fall of the Giants, was moved down from the room above around 1700, replacing an earlier stucco ceiling. A speaking-tube leads to the room above, and another, from c. 1705, leads from the window niche in the east wall to the gable room at the opposite end. The bays were added in 1758. In front of the bay to the right stood Christian IV's famous arrangement for raising and lowering the drawbridge. The King lay in state here, and most of the exhibits are from his time.

101. Goblet in the form of a young knight (Christian IV), tilting at the ring. Made by the goldsmith Heinrich Beust in Brunswick in 1598, commissioned by the King and paid for with the prizes he had won at tilting during the coronation celebrations. The names and arms of the King's fellow competitors are engraved on the columns. When Christian IV had to sell his royal plate after the defeat of 1628, he kept two pieces, a christening present – and this goblet.
102. Bronze bust of Christian IV, modelled 1643 in Copenhagen by François Dieussart and cast in Glückstadt in 1650.

103. Renaissance chairs, upholstery as no. 212.
104. Stools as no. 213.
105. Table with stone top, in which are cut lines for a game, probably originally intended for use as a calculating board, but also used as a »shove-halfpenny« board. Foot from 18th century.
106. Astronomical clock with musical works and moving figures; made in 1594 by Isaac Habrecht, one of the makers of the famous clock in Strasbourg Cathedral; it is partly a copy of this.
107. Marble bust of King Charles I of England (1600-49). Made in 1633, probably by Pierre Besnier.
108. Marble bust of Queen Henriette Marie of England (1609-69), King Charles I's Queen. Made in 1640 by F. Dieussart.
109. Calendar table, dated 1638. On the cover a portrait of Christian IV, by Adrian Muiltjes?

Room 2. Christian IV's Writing Closet

In this tower room, which was easily heated, Christian IV carried on his vast correspondence. The room has been preserved more or less intact since the time of Christian IV, with features such as the ceiling paintings illustrating scenes from the Italian epic Orlando Furioso, the paintings inlaid in the panels, and the fireplace. The wall-coverings of green silk printed with gold designs date from c. 1700.

In the extension to this room Sophie Amalie, Frederik III's Queen, installed a novelty: an *ascenseur*, or ascending chair, which connected the ground floor with the upper storeys. The study contains mementos of Christian IV and his forefathers.

201. Painting of Christ as »The Man of Sorrows«. Christian IV's vision at Rodenburg, 8th December 1625, with his own handwritten description.
202. Prince Christian, the Prince Elect, on horseback; in the background, his father, as in no. 103. Painted by Adrian Muiltjes c. 1635-39.
203. Christian IV on horseback in front of Kronborg Castle; in the background, the Prince Elect, on horseback, as in no. 102. Same painter as above.
204. Carved head of a stag, with the antlers of the stag which, on 28th December 1611, alarmed by the advancing Swedes, fled

into the Danish camp in Kalmar and thus warned the army.
205. Christian IV, half-length portrait, painted by Jacob van Doordt about 1611.
206. Christian II (1481-1559; King 1513-23). Painted on wood; old copy from Quentin Massys.
207. Frederik I (1471-1533; King 1523). Painted on wood.
208. Painting of Queen Anne Cathrine's dog, with her monogram on its collar, dated 1598.
209. Christian IV c. 1612. Painted by Pieter Isaacsz.
210. Clock with moving figures: the Emperor and the seven Electors. German, late 16th century.
211. Cabinet of ebony, with reliefs of gilt bronze and engraved metal plates with copies of Virgilius Solis's biblical illustrations from 1560. The cabinet was presumably made in Augsburg; it is dated 1580. The pedestal is modern.
212. Renaissance chair upholstered in silk velvet brocade interwoven with the King's cipher, C4.
213. Stools carved by Christian Nerger c. 1690, upholstered as no. 212.
214. Brass andirons from Christian IV's last years.
215. Window-pane with the coat-of-arms of Holstein-Gottorp, and the name of Duke Johan-Adolph of Holstein-Gottorp (1575-1616), brother-in-law of Christian IV.
216. Fountain cock in the shape of Neptune riding on a dolphin. 17th century. From the »Hermitage« (now the Hercules Pavilion) in The King's Garden (Kongens Have).
217. Ellen Marsvin (1572-1649), Kirsten Munk's mother. Half-length, dated 1648, painted by Karel van Mander.
218. Portrait of Frederik II's widow, the Dowager Queen Sophie. Detail of a full-length portrait painted by Pieter Isaacsz, c. 1610-15.
219. Christian IV. Painting signed: A.M. (Adrian Muiltjes?), 1638.
220. Queen Sophie, wife of Frederik II, née Duchess of Mecklenburg (1557-1631); married in 1572. The Queen is probably wearing her wedding costume and crown of gold with white pearls. Painted by Hans Knieper 1578?
221. Christian IV as a boy; painted about 1585 by Hans Knieper.
222. Alabaster relief of Frederik II, made after the death of the King (1588) by Gert van Egen?
223. Tin mug; part of Princess Sophie Elisabeth's dowry, 1632. Found by excavation in Gothersgade.
224. Tin plate from among the wedding presents given by Christian IV to his son, Hans Ulrik Gyldenløve, in 1638.
225. Mug of stoneware, with the Danish arms. Rhenish work, 1623.
226.-227. Brass ornamental dish and bronze chafing-dish; part of Leonora Christina's dowry, 1636.

228. Silver lantern made for Christian IV by the Copenhagen gold-smith Hans Trægaard.

229. Silver cup with Kirsten Munk's coat-of-arms and name; the hallmark of Hamburg and the maker's mark of Hermann Lambrecht.

230. Silver mug, with Kirsten Munk's name and coat-of-arms and the year 1653. Made by Daniel Harder in Odense.

231. Tankard of silver in the form of a manikin. The handle in the form of two entwined monkeys. Stamped AB, presumably for Arent van Bolten, Amsterdam 1608.

232. The Psalms of David, bound in silver, with David playing the harp.

233. Covered cup of silver made for Christian IV in 1600 by Gabriel Brockmüller in Hillerød as the prize in a wager with four courtiers; he who became intoxicated first was the loser. Known as the Temperance Cup.

234. Two salt cellars of Wanli porcelain, set in brass gilt with pearls, turquoises and precious stones. From c. 1610?

235. King Christian IV's seal, used in the Court of Justice. 1630.

236. King Christian IV's privy seal.

237. The seal of the town of Christiansstad (in Scania).

238. Two dog collars of leather. Belonged to the Electress Hedevig of Saxony (1581-1641), Christian IV's sister.

239. Two small bedside lamps of silver and rock-crystal in the shape of ships. Christian IV period.

240. Christian IV and Queen Anne Cathrine, silver plaquettes in frame of later date; attributed to Nicolaus Svabe, after J.v. Doordt.

241. Christian IV's compass, from 1595, of silver gilt.

242. Miniature on copper of Frederik III when young.

243. Grass snake's head with Salzburger guilder. According to the Kunstkammer (Cabinet of Curiosities) inventory, found by Frederik III near Frederiksborg after the Swedish siege. Another tradition from the last century has it that Christian IV dropped the coin while out walking near Frederiksborg. The King cut off the snake's head, but it kept its hold on the coin.

244. Christian IV, painted by A. Magerstadt?

245. Christian IV. Enamelled miniature on gold, c. 1640. By unknown artist.

246. Coin balance; gilt silver; used by Christian IV.

247. Table clock made 1561 by Steffen Brenner; presented to Christian IV by his father in 1584: the dial was restored under Frederik V.

248. Portrait of Christian IV in wax repoussé, c. 1640.

249. A stick made of a narwhal tusk; with the name of Duke Wilhelm of Saxe-Weimar (1598-1662) and the date 1641.

Room 3. Christian IV's Bedroom

The King died here on 28th February 1648. This room, together with the two preceding rooms, constituted his private chambers. During the reign of Frederik III, the room became incorporated in Queen Sophie Amalie's suite.

The wall panels and doors are from Christian IV's time and originally had floral-painted framing. In the 1660's the wall panels and doors were painted in the »Chinese« style by the Dutchman, Francis de Bray, for the fashion-conscious Sophie Amalie. The green-lacquered panels bear gold line drawings of landscapes, boats, and interiors based on descriptions of China by Jan Nieuhof (1665), Athanasius Kircher (1667), and older Chinese novels, Shuihu Zhuan (Tales from the River's Brink, 14th cent.) and San Guo Zhi (Stones of the Three Kingdoms.). The frames are of imitation tortoiseshell with silver mouldings. The stucco ceiling dates from the 1630's. The three inset ceiling paintings depict the gods of earth, heaven and ocean. The first and third of these were painted by Isaac Isaacsz; the central ceiling panel, showing Hera and Zeus on Olympus, was painted by Abraham Wuchters. Hera has been made to resemble Sophie Amalie – the first Absolutist's Queen to have herself depicted as the Mother of the Gods.

This room contains portraits and curios owned by Christian IV.

allegorical representations engraved on silver plates (from H. Goltzius and D. Vinckboons). The silver plates engraved by Simon de Pas, c. 1624?

304. Christian IV on his death-bed. Painted by Bernt Hilwaerts, 1648.

305. Chest with iron mountings bearing the intertwined names of Christian IV and Queen Anne Cathrine and the date 1599.

306. Two-handed sword; on the blade, Christian IV's name.

307. Chinese porcelain figures; placed in this room in the time of Queen Charlotte Amalie.

308. Prince Christian, the Prince Elect. Painted on wood by Karel van Mander 1642.

309. The Prince Elect's consort, Magdalena Sibylla, born the Electoral Princess of Saxony. Painted on wood by Karel van Mander, 1642.

310. Portrait of Christian IV. Embroidered by Clas Harder.

311. Copper plate for the large engraving of Christian IV; engraved by A. Haelwegh from K. van Mander's painting.

312. Duke Ulrik, youngest son of Christian IV (16ll-33). Painted on wood. Copy from about 1660 by Wolfgang Heimbach.

313. Queen Anne Cathrine and her eldest son, Christian, the King Elect. Painted by Jacob van Doordt, 1611.

314. Bone and amber model of Rosenborg. Made by Niels Nielsen, c. 1750.

315. Hedevig, Electress of Saxony, sister of Christian IV. Gilded brass plate, engraved by D. Kellerthaler.

316. Leonora Christina, Countess of Schleswig and Holstein (1621-98), Christian IV's daughter; wife of Count Corfitz Ulfeld, the Seneschal. Modern copy.

317. Christian IV, painted on wood by David Bailly c. 1627.

318. Casket with ink-pad, and a seal bearing the King's monogram in facsimile. Before 1645.

319. Marsyas and Apollo. Ivory relief from 1624 bearing coat-of-arms of Holstein-Gottorp, signed: (joined) H. O. and H. V. (Hans Ochs in Husum).

320. Christian IV's blood-stained clothes from the naval battle of Kolberger Heide, 1st July 1644: a black-and-purple jerkin of silk velvet with a blood-stained lace collar and cuff. Right shoulder pierced by bullet.
Cap of coloured silk with Tønder lace. Lining marked C 4 and 1642. Pierced by shot.
The King's blood-stained handkerchief, embroidered with C 4 1644.
Embroidered cap of pale-green satin; a piece of green taffeta has been fastened to it serving as a patch for the King's blinded eye.
Shirt with lace border; embroidered with C 4 1644. Pillow-

case with Tønder lace, blood-stained embroidered with C4.
A pair of eardrops in the form of enamelled white hands, which hold a piece of bronze and a piece of iron; fragments of a burst Danish cannon and a Swedish ball which were removed from the King's forehead and eye after the naval battle of Kolberger Heide. Worn by Vibeke Kruse.

Room 4. The Dark Room

This room was originally connected with the Stone Passage (Room 7) and served as an antechamber dividing the King's apartments from those of the Queen at the south end of the palace. In 1616, with the building of the Great Tower where Christian IV installed his bathroom with running water, the room lost some of the direct daylight. In 1705 it became the bedchamber of the King and Queen. The stucco ceiling, which is original, was made by Valentin Dresler from Schmalkalden. The fireplace with mirror and the silk wall-coverings date from the time of Frederik IV: the striped wall-coverings with scalloped pelmets and tassels were probably modelled after the Dutchman Daniel Marot's designs for decorating the finest houses of the day. The armchair from the 17th century was ingeniously constructed to grasp a guest with concealed tentacles in the armrests. The strapped person could then be soaked by water running from a vessel in the back of the chair through channels in the seat. When the victim had been released and was getting up from the chair, a trumpet concealed in the seat would toot. Through the window on the right may be seen Christian IV's lavatory, which was covered with blue and white glazed tiles in 1705.

401. Wax bust of Frederik III. The cabinet was made by Dietrich Schäffer 1742-43.
402. Wax bust of Prince Jørgen, made by Antoine Benoist in Paris, 1669. Cabinet by court cabinet-maker Hans Balche.
403. Wax bust of Sophie Amalie. By Antoine Benoist? The cabinet by Dietrich Schäffer 1742-43.
404. Ebony cabinet, covered on the inside with tortoiseshell inlaid

with flowers of bone, and with a carved representation of two dancing peasants, after an engraving by Albrecht Dürer. C. 1650.

Room 5. The Marble Room. (Frederik III's Room)

Originally the bedroom of Christian IV's morganatic wife, Kirsten Munk. In 1663-67 Frederik III furnished it in a pompous Baroque style to celebrate the introduction of Absolutism in 1660. The ceiling was stuccoed and the walls covered with imitation marble, probably by the Italian, Francesco Bruno. The ceiling paintings show putti bearing the regalia; in the heart-shaped areas surrounding the paintings various parts of the Danish coat-of-arms are shown. In this Audience Chamber, Christian V, whose monogram is on one of the doors, bestowed the Order of Dannebrog for the very first time; among the recipients were Griffenfeld and Cort Adeler. The newly-founded Supreme Court was also opened in this room.

The furniture, some of which shows the French influence during Absolutism, is contemporary with the fixed room decorations, and some of it belongs to the original furnishing.

501. Silver mug with ivory carvings, based in part on mythological scenes by Rubens. Some of them are attributed to Joachim Henne.
502. Silver cup presented to a member of the deputation from Bornholm, who handed over the island to King Frederik III in 1658. Made by Michael Kabes of Nuremberg.
503. Tankards of silver with inlaid Holstein coins with nettle leaves, lions on the covers, and feet in the form of the collared swans of Stormarn. Made for Hamburg's projected acclamation of Frederik III in 1654 (nos. 2111, 5156-5160). The cup is stamped with the mark of the goldsmith Jørgen Stilke.
504. Frederik III as Roman emperor, wearing the Order of the Elephant; mother-of-pearl inlaid in an oval leaf of slate; frame of gilt chased copper. Attributed to Jeremias Hercules.
505. Frederik III, engraved in mother-of-pearl; attributed to Jeremias Hercules.
506. Two masque figures of coloured glass on a framework of

metal thread (comedy figures, morra players). Early 17th century Venetian work.

507. Box with a piece of alchemic gold which Frederik III is supposed to have produced with the help of Guiseppe Burrhi, an Italian alchemist.

508. Two seals, enamel ascribed to Paul Kurtz.

509. Five signet rings of gold, belonged to Frederik III.

510. Chess pieces of slate including Kings Frederik III and Carl X Gustav of Sweden and their consorts.

511. Nautilus cup bearing engravings of Frederik III on horseback; the Siege of Copenhagen, and the Battle in the Sound. Engraved by J. Hercules, 1671?

512. Pomander (perfume container) made of walnut, with carved portraits of Frederik III and Sophie Amalie, made in 1660 by the medallist Johan Blum?

513. Fourteen miniature portraits of Frederik III, enamelled by Paul Prieur 1666-69.

514. Animal group in wax; an elephant shaking off its keeper and tossing aside an ibex. Allegorical representation of the victory over Stenbock's Swedish army at Nyborg, 1659.

515. Queen Christina of Sweden (1626-1689). Enamelled miniature by Pierre Signac.

516. Pomander of silver with six sliding lids, bearing the portrait of Charles I (King of England until 1649).

517. Four boats carved in ivory by Jacob Jensen Nordmand, Frederik III's armourer.

518. Four oval silver plates, with chased figurative representations in exceptionally high relief. Hamburg, c. 1650?

519. Portrait of Jacob Jensen Nordmand (1614-95) on wood. Signed: Wolfgang Heimbach 1654.

520. The frigate »Norwegian Lion«, carved model in ivory 1654 by Jacob Jensen Nordmand.

521. To boats carved in ivory, galleys, by Jacob Jensen Nordmand, Frederik III's armourer. Made from a drawing by Cort Adeler, Danish admiral, formerly on Venetian service.

522. Cabinet set of five vases, with lacque brillante work by Queen Louise, wife of Frederik IV. Displayed in the Marble Room 1718.

523. Cabinet covered with tortoiseshell and inlaid with silver ornaments. Antwerp, c. 1680? In the marble room in 1696.

524. Queen Sophie Amalie: oval, painted by Abraham Wuchters.

525. Frederik III: oval, painted on wood; from the studio of Karel van Mander.

526. Equestrian statuette of silver: Frederik III tilting at the ring. The figure is driven by clockwork. Made in Copenhagen by Jørgen Stichmand, c. 1650?

527. Jewel cabinet of ebony and ivory, inlaid with Florentine mo-

saic; made in Augsburg; stamped with the coat-of-arms of the town, and the word: Eben.

528. Two carved guéridons, of gilded and blue-painted wood. Monogram of Queen Sophie Amalie on the pedestal. Top of artificial marble (scagliola) with the coats-of-arms of Denmark and Lüneburg. Matching table, bearing the Queen's motto: En Dieu mon Esperance: My hope in God. Foot made in Copenhagen by Jean L'Estienne, top by Ottavio Carone 1672? Saved from the fire at Sophie Amalienborg in 1689.

529. Table, semi-precious stones from Christian IV's Oratory in Frederiksborg Palace chapel. Top made in Prague, 1600-1620? Later foot, from c. 1660. On the frame Frederik III's monogram and motto: Dominus providebit (the Lord will provide).

530. Equestrian statuette carved in iron; represents the Emperor Leopold of Germany (1640-1705); Made by Gottfried Leigebe 1659-60.

531. Ebony cabinet decorated with Florentine mosaics and marble.

532. Two drinking horns of ivory mounted in silver gilt. One of the horns bears Frederik III's monogram.

533. Ivory busts attributed to Joachim Henne, 1667: Duke Frederik III and Duchess Marie Elisabeth of Holstein-Gottorp.

534. Coconut with Frederik III's monogram. Signed: Th. Broughton fecit.

535. Portrait relief in coloured enamel. Duke Christian Albrecht of Holstein-Gottorp.

536. Two portrait reliefs in coloured enamel. Duchess Frederikke Amalie.

537. Drinking horn of ivory mounted in silver gilt. Decorated with battling sea creatures. On the cover a Nereid, and stem depicting Neptune and Amphitrite. German, c. 1670.

538. Small jug of narwhal tusk with Frederik III's monogram and head of a moor with ear-pearls. Signed: J(acob) J(ensen) Nordmand, 16)51.

539. Drinking horn of rhinocerus with two Bacchus figures of ivory. On the body a hunting scene.

Room 6. The King's Chamber (Christian V's Room)

This was originally Kirsten Munk's room, but from Frederik III's time it became part of the King's suite (an antechamber to the Marble Room). The fireplace is from Christian IV's time and is surmounted by a portrait of Christian V in his later years, painted by

Jacob d'Agar. The fireplace was originally in Room 10, but was moved here after a re-building around 1700, when the ceiling also acquired its present appearance. Several artists were involved. The central painting, (from Christian IV's time, possibly painted by Francis Cleyn) represents a group of musicians playing, and may be from one of the music pavillions in The King's Garden. Benoît le Coffre has supposedly painted part of the outer frieze and the two pieces of the inner frieze with the dancing and playing children. At the end of the 17th century the walls were covered with tapestries (signed M.Wauters), which Christian V purchased in the Netherlands.

601. Box of amber with ivory reliefs showing pastoral scenes. 17th century. By Gottfred Wolffram c. 1707.
602. Prince Jørgen (George), King Christian V's brother, consort of Queen Anne of England. Marble relief.
603. Christian V. Alabaster statuette.
604. Duke August Frederik of Holstein-Gottorp; Prince Bishop of Lübeck (1646-1705). Ivory relief, by Joachim Henne.
605. Four enamelled medallions with representations of the Virtues. Signed: J. Barbette 1695.
606. Silver seal portraying Christian V sitting on the throne, which now stands in the Long Hall; three lions can be seen in front. Made by Jeremias Hercules.
607. Silver box portraying Christian V sitting on the throne.
608. An egg mounted in silver filigree, with the monograms of Christian V and Charlotte Amalie.
609. Hans Leth, Chaplain-in-Ordinary, (1625-88). Miniature in enamel, signed: Prieur 1675.
610. Prince Jørgen, brother of Christian V. Miniature in enamel by Barbette.
611. Ivory box with portrait of a man in wax repoussé made by Ulrik Christian Gyldenløve in 1692.
612. A piece of alchemic gold, and the lead from which it was made by the Landgrave of Hesse-Homburg.
613. Ulrikke Eleonore, Queen of Sweden, sister of King Christian V. Enamelled miniature in frame of silver filigree.
614. Christian V and Queen Charlotte Amalie; mother-of- pearl inlaid in ebony.
615. Frederik IV as Prince? c. 1690. Oil on metal.
616. Ulrikke Eleonore, King Christian V's sister, Queen of Sweden (1656-93). Enamelled miniature, signed: J. B(arbette) 1694.

617. Peder Griffenfeld (1635-99). Enamelled miniature, signed: Prieur 1673.
618. Peder Griffenfeld (1635-99). Enamelled miniature signed: Prieur 1675.
619. Medallion of ivory with portrait of Christian V, signed: J.henne (16) 89. On the reverse a lion guarding the escutcheons of Denmark, Norway and Schleswig, and the inscription: (the lion) covers, protects and shields. Made to commemorate the incorporation of Schleswig into Denmark, 1685-89.
620. Eight crystal studs mounted in gold and enamel, used for ornamenting clothes and fastened with a ribbon to the shoulder.
621. Christian V. Enamelled miniature by unknown artist.
622. Christian V. Enamelled miniature, signed: Prieur 1681.
623. Christian V. Miniature in oils by Abraham Wuchters?
624. Queen Charlotte Amalie. Enamelled miniature painted by J. Barbette.
625. Christian V. Miniature in enamel, by Prieur? A gift to Hans Leth, Chaplain-in-Ordinary, (1625-88).
626. Christian V. Enamelled miniature, signed: Prieur 1681.
627. Two gold rings with Christian V's portrait in enamel.
628. A gold ring and two signet rings of silver gilt. Belonged to Christian V.
629. Signet ring of gold, the plate of ruby. Engraved with the device of the Hoppe family and the letters I.H. Belonged to Vice Admiral Iver Hoppe, who saved Christian V's life with his anchor during a storm in the Baltic Sea in 1677 (cf no. 766).
630. Gilded chair from the Knights' Chapel at Frederiksborg with legs in the shape of elephants' trunks. Carved by C. Nerger 1694.
631. Wine-cooler of mottled marble.
632. Dedication to Christian V from »Your majesty's most humble and loyal subject«, Johannes Laverentzen (c. 1648-1729), the royal scribe, who wrote out The Danish Law of King Christian V for the Record Office.
633. The coloured engraving of Christian IV which his daughter, Leonora Christina Ulfeld, sent to Christian V, 1685, appealing for her release from prison.
634. Set of hunting daggers, with the monogram of Prince Christian, the Prince Elect. Made by Gabriel Gipfel or his studio in Dresden c. 1630.
635. Two falcon hoods; falconer's bag, and lure.
636. Christian V's hunting horn.
637. A bone, which had been held by a citizen and pierced twice by King Christian V during a visit to Varde, in order to show his skill as a marksman.

638. Two gilded plaster impressions of Christian V's royal seal. Made by Anton Meybusch, 1690's.

639. Two silver stamps of Christian V's royal seal, set in brass. Made by an unknown medallist, 1690's.

640. Chalice with lid and silver gilt paten, engraved with Queen Charlotte Amalie's monogram. Made in Cassel by Johannes Riese.

641. The entry into Dresden of Princess Anne Sophie as Electoral Princess, 1666. Gilt, engraved copperplate, signed: Davit Conrad fecit.

642. The alliance between Frederik III and Johann Georg II, 1663. On the columns the coat-of-arms of Denmark and Saxony. In the background prospects of Copenhagen and Dresden. Gilt, engraved copperplate, signed: D. Conrad fecit.

643. A backgammon game. Wooden box with reliefs, inside decorated with inlaid wood. 15 pieces of light and 15 pieces of dark wood. Made in Eger, Hungary, c. 1660.

644. Two silver chafing dishes with the King's and Queen's monograms: made by I.H. de Moor, Copenhagen 1690.

645. Two silver andirons with Christian V's monogram: made by I.H. de Moor, Copenhagen 1690?

646. Table and two guéridons with mirror to match, of bluepainted wood, with silver filigree ornaments in which can be seen Queen Charlotte Amalie's monogram. Originally lacquered in black with Frederik III's monogram. France, 1669.

647. Hunting cup; a silver bowl placed between the twenty-point antlers of a stag.

648. Showcase containing exhibits from the Kunstkammer; the trophies in the lower part are furnished with Christian V's monogram. The case presumably originates from the Kunstkammer and contained a wax bust of Christian V.

649. Miniature bust of Christian V, modelled in wax and signed: H A(ren) F(eld).

650. Christian V, silver bust, on a round pedestal. Made by the King's goldsmith Jørgen Kurtz, 1697.

651. Jug of amber, with carved Bacchic scenes and the Virtues. German inscription. Presumably from Königsberg c. 1650.

652. Wooden cup, with King Christian V's and Queen Charlotte Amalie's monogram; on the lid, three rampant lions carrying a crown. Norwegian work, carved by Halvor Fanden?

653. Cup of birch-wood, with Christian V's monogram. Signed: M(agnus) B(erg) (16)90.

654. Christian V, drawn in letters and coloured. Signed: I. Henne Inventor et pinxit 1692.

655. Christian V and Queen Charlotte Amalie, painted by Jacob d'Agar.

656. English lamp-clock, made in London by Henry Harper (master, 1664-1708).
657. Japanese lacquered cupboard on richly carved, gilded foot from the time of Christian V with the Danish and Hessian coats-of-arms. Table foot carved by Christian Nerger?
658. The Electress Anna Sophie of Saxony, sister of Christian V; painted on copper by Abraham Wuchters.
659. The Electress Wilhelmine Ernestine of Pfalz, sister of King Christian V; painted on copper by Abraham Wuchters.
660. Two grisailles of Christian V, painted by Abr. Wuchters?
661. Ivory goblet, with picture of an Emperor triumphant (Ferdinand III?).
662. Sixteen-foil beaker of turned ivory. On the cover, Bacchus above, the Judgement of Paris below.
663. Beaker of ivory with rural scene. Ascribed to Gottfried Wolfram.
664. Flagon cut in rock crystal by C. Labert.
665. Boat-shaped goblet of rock crystal with frog on the lid; mounting of enamelled gold. Made in Milan at the end of the 16th century. The engraved decoration made by Annibale Fontana?
666. Galley-shaped boat of rock crystal illustrating the Feast of Neptune. Made in the Saracchi studio in Milan c. 1580. The foot is probably not the original; the gilded mounting is from the 18th century.
667. Bowl on a foot of rock crystal, with pipes and leaves; made in Milan c. 1580. The enamelled gold mounting with turquoises is from the 17th century.
668. Tankard carved in ivory, with handle and lining of silver gilt. On the cover, a couple seated on a wine cask, on the body, garden scenes with courting couple. Mounting stamped Lübeck, c. 1650. Master: CPM?
669. Mercury, carved in ivory. Ascribed to Joachim Henne.
670. Tureen, of Japanese porcelain, decorated in blue, with silver mounting; the lid bears Queen Charlotte Amalie's monogram and crown; supposedly porcelain brought home with the first cargo of the new Danish East India Company (founded 1670).
671. Leda and the Swan, statuette carved in ivory. Ascribed to Joachim Henne. Foot of wood adorned with silver ornaments, ball feet of coral.
672. Jewel box of chased gilt silver, ornamented with about two thousand small diamonds. In the bottom, chased relief of The Judgement of Paris. Supposedly a present from the subsequent Queen Anne of England, to her mother-in-law, Queen Sophie Amalie. The box was stolen in 1794 during the Christiansborg fire, but the thief was apprehended.

673. Two table decorations of silver gilt, with reliefs of ivory, depicting, respectively, the Queen of Sheba at the Court of King Solomon and the Judgement of Solomon. Hamburg work from c. 1650? Found at the palace at Kiel c. 1829.

674. Four table decorations of ivory and silver gilt. The bowls are supported, respectively, by three she-fauns and the four elements, three fauns and the four seasons, Mars and Venus, and Apollo and Daphne.

675. Mars going off to war while Venus, helped by Amor, tries to hold him back. Ivory, ascribed to Joachim Henne.

Room 7. The Stone Passage

The long passage connecting the two big gable rooms on the ground floor has originally been divided into two antechambers. The stucco of the ceiling is different at the two ends of the passage; at the northern end it is from the time of Christian IV. When the stair turret was built at the middle of the eastern side of the palace in 1633, a spiral staircase was built leading from the first floor only to the remaining storeys, whereas the ground floor of the stair turret was used as a silver room with access from the Stone Passage. In 1758 a spiral staircase was built in, now giving access to the palace's first floor.

A complete list of exhibited weapons is to be found at the back of the guide, p. 103.

701. Antlers of a wounded stag to which, in 1698, Christian V gave the deathblow; in its fall it knocked the King over and he was badly hurt.

702. Christian IV's genealogical table with his ancestors' portraits and coats-of-arms; from about 1610.

705. The victorious Christian IV on horseback with Kalmar Castle in the background. By unknown artist, c. 1613.

706. Christian IV as commander-in-chief. Sketch for the large equestrian portrait at Frederiksborg Palace. By Karel van Mander c. 1642-44.

707. Christian IV on horseback in civilian dress with Frederiksborg Palace in the background. By unknown artist, after Karel van Mander, c. 1644.

708. Christian IV as mediator in the Thirty Years' War. Allegorical grisaille painting from 1643; signed: Adrian v(an de) Venne.

709.-710. Bronze busts of Frederik II and Queen Sophie. By J.G.

van der Schardt, 1578-79. Bought by Frederik VI during the Congress of Vienna, 1815.

711. The storming of Copenhagen, 11.2.1659. Painting, signed: D(aniel) Vertangen.

712. Paying homage to the Hereditary King in front of the Castle of Copenhagen, 18th October, 1660. Signed: Wolfg. Heimbach fec. Oldenborg 1666.

713. Paying homage to the Hereditary King before the Castle of Copenhagen 1660: seen from Holmen's Bridge. Painted by Michael van Haven.

714. Christian IV's vision before the Battle of Listerdyb, 1644. Painting illustrating the King's dream of an honourable resurrection the night before his victory over the superior Swedish-Dutch fleet. Unknown artist.

715. Christian IV on horseback in front of Rosenborg; beside the King, an architect (Hans von Steenwinckel?) or an engineer. Painted about 1638, by Karel van Mander?

716. Christian IV's eldest son Christian, the Prince Elect, (1603-47). Equestrian painting by unknown artist, c. 1635.

717. Ludvig Munk of Nørlund (1537-160?), Governor of Norway, Kirsten Munk's father, painted by Gerrit Cornelisz(?).

718. Portrait of Queen Anne of England, sister of Christian IV. By unknown artist.

719. Portrait of Princess Maria of Russia; married to Duke Magnus, son of Christian III.

720. Valdemar Christian, Count of Schleswig and Holstein (1622-56), Christian IV's son with Kirsten Munk. Full-length portrait by Karel van Mander.

721. Frederik II's sister Anna, the Electress of Saxony (1532-85). Painted by Zach. Wehme, c. 1585.

722. Presumably Frederik II's daughter, Elisabeth, Duchess of Brunswick-Wolfenbüttel (1573-1626). Half-length portrait.

723. Jørgen Rosenkrants. Councillor of State (1523-1596). Probably painted by Tobias Gemperlin c. 1590. Unsigned.

724. Ivory busts attributed to Joachim Henne, 1667: Duke Christian Albrecht of Holstein-Gottorp and Frederik III, Christian V and Queen Charlotte Amalie.

725. Portrait of Christian IV as a young man.

726. King Christian V's portrait embroidered by Leonora Christina Ulfeld in Maribo Convent, 1686.

727. Duke Christian Albrecht of Holstein-Gottorp (1641-94). Painting signed: L. Weyandt fecit Kiel 1697.

728. Family group: Count Anton Günther of Oldenborg, his consort, and his natural son, Count Anton of Aldenburg, painted 1667 by Wolfgang Heimbach in Copenhagen.

729. Reliefs in ivory with motifs from the Bible and Ovid's Metamorphoses. Made by Joachim Henne c. 1665-90.

730. Table with top of inlaid semi-precious stones on black foot; from the period of Christian V.

731. Clock kept in motion by a ball rolling down a spiral. Presented to Frederik III by the Duke of Holstein-Gottorp, 1655?

732. Painting of Count Anton Günther of Oldenborg's wonder horse, Kranich. Unknown artist.

733.-734. Count Anton Günther of Oldenborg (1583-1667), upon whose death Oldenborg and Delmenhorst would fall to Denmark, and his consort, Sophie Catharine, Princess of Sønderborg (1617-1696); painted on wood by Wolfgang Heimbach. Four of King Frederik III's children, painted on copper, presumably by Toussaint Gelton:

735. Frederikke Amalie (1649-1704), Duchess of Holstein-Gottorp.

736. Wilhelmine Ernestine (1650-1706), Electress of Pfalz.

737. Anna Sophie (1647-1717), Electress of Saxony.

738. Jørgen (George) 1653-1708), Prince Consort of England, Duke of Cumberland.

739. Portrait of the Electress Wilhelmine Ernestine of Pfalz, daughter of Frederik III. Ascribed to Johan Georg Wagner.

740. Portrait of Carl X Gustav's Queen, Hedevig Eleonore. By unknown artist.

741. Ebony cabinet with Frederik III's and Sophie Amalie's monograms on the inside of the doors.

742. Ivory reliefs with portraits of members of the Royal Family during the reign of Christian V; carved by Joachim Henne, Jean Cavalier, Gottfried Wolffram and Wilhelm Heinrich Wessel.

743. Plate inlaid with coloured semi-precious stones. Frederik III's coat-of-arms as Prince-Archbishop of Bremen.

744. Gouache paintings by Christian V's daughter, Sophie Hedevig; in silver filigree frames.

745. Gouache painting representing the Abduction of Ganymede, painted by King Christian V, and signed: C.5 1673.

746. Coronation of Christian V, 1671. Painting by Michael van Haven?

747. Christian V's breastplate and helmet used for »carrousel« riding; of gilded brass.

748. The Elector Friedrich Wilhelm (the Great) of Brandenburg (1620-88). Painting on copper, presumably by P. Nason.

749. The Electress Wilhelmine Ernestine of Pfalz, daughter of Frederik III. Painted on copper. Signed: Toussaint Gelton fc. 1677.

750. Portrait of Frederik III kneeling during the battle of Nyborg; painted by Wolfgang Heimbach, 1659. Signed.

751. Portrait of Christian V by unknown artist.

752. Prince Jørgen (George) (1653-1708), Christian V's brother; Prince Consort of England, married to Anne, who succeeded to the throne of England. Three-quarter portrait after John Riley.

The stair turret between the 1st and 2nd floor

753. Frederik III and Sophie Amalie on horseback, painted in the centre of a wreath of flowers, probably by O. Elliger, c. 1655.
754. The Vicar of Jork in the diocese of Bremen; said to have been painted by Frederik III in his youth, when he was Prince-Archbishop of Bremen.
755. Young cavalier in shepherd's costume, probably a situation from a court masque. Unknown artist, c. 1650.
756. Christian V as a child. Painted on wood by W. Heimbach.
757. Queen Sophie Amalie in the costume of a peasant girl by Wolfgang Heimbach. Full-length painting on wood.
758. Two drawings from the middle of the 18th century representing the gold horns (from c. 500), found in 1639 and 1734 respectively.
759. Portrait of Christian V, painted by Abraham Wuchters, c. 1670.
760. Count Anton Günther of Oldenborg (1583-1667). Embroidery.
761. Queen Sophie Amalie, consort of Frederik III. Three-quarter length, by Abraham Wuchters.
762. Peder Schumacher, Count of Griffenfeld (1635-99); Chancellor. Painted on wood by A. Wuchters.
763. Christian V with his sons, Frederik, Christian, and Carl. Made after the painting by Jacob d'Agar in Frederiksborg Council Chamber.
764. Christian V, painted by Abraham Wuchters, c. 1670.
765. Copenhagen as seen from the northwest. Water-colour drawing from the late 17th century by W. Riboldt.
766. Anchor of iron; supposed to have saved the life of Christian V in a storm in the Baltic; bears a verse of thanksgiving by Thomas Kingo (cf no. 629).
767. Christian V conversing with his half-brother, Ulrik Frederik Gyldenløve, and Count Anton of Aldenburg (1633-80). Grisaille, probably by Anton Steenwinckel.
768. Portrait of Christian V, signed: F. Douven 1696.
770. »Carrousel« paintings from the time of Christian V. The first painting shows the King himself.

The stair turret between the 2nd and 3rd floor

771. A number of equestrian pictures depicting the haute école of the 1690's. In the background, the Royal Danish castles. The first painting is of Christian V in front of Copenhagen Castle.
772. Flower paintings on parchment, executed in the latter part of the 17th century by Maria Sybilla Merian.

Room 8. Frederik IV's Corridor

The walls are covered with gilt leather tapestries from Frederiksborg Palace. The exhibits and paintings mainly date from the time of Frederik IV, among them mementos from the last great war with Sweden under Carl XII. In an 18th century showcase there is a collection of ivories exhibited in the same manner as in the Kunstkammer.

801. Magnus Stenbock, Swedish commander. Self-portrait, painted in captivity and sent to Frederik IV together with a painting of a chicken run, a view of Tønningen (where he was captured) and the inscription: Herr lasz deinen Gefangenen losz. (See no. 1023).
802. King Carl XII of Sweden (1682-1718; King 1697). Copy after David von Krafft?
803. Carl XII's rapier, which he presented to the brave Colonel Ulrik Christian Kruse (1666-1727), who was taken prisoner at Høland, Norway, in 1716.
804. The coronation of Frederik IV in the chapel of Frederiksborg Palace, 1700. Water-colour by Bendix Grodtschilling III, 1706.
805. King Carl XII of Sweden (1682-1718) and his sister, Hedevig Sophie, Duchess of Holstein-Gottorp. Child portrait, full-length, by David Klöcker von Ehrenstrahl 1687.
806. The town of Stade surrendering to Frederik IV, 1712. Painting.
807. Queen Louise, painted by Jacob d'Agar.
808. Frederik IV in his coronation robes; small, full-length painting, attributed to B. le Coffre.
811. Prince Wilhelm, son of Christian V. Half-length, painted by Anton Schoonjans 1696.
812. View of Copenhagen, 1702. Woven in silk. Signed: Jochim Wriede 1702, and: H.J. Petersen fecit.

813. Frederik IV as Prince. Full-length painting by Jacob d'Agar.
814. Queen Ulrikke Eleonore of Sweden, King Christian V's sister (1656-93). Half-length. Signed: D. Klöcker Ehrenstrahl Ao. 1681.
815. Frederik IV. Half-length portrait; painted by Hendrik Krock?
816. Queen Louise. Half-length portrait; Copy after Jacob d'Agar?
817. Cups, centre-pieces and statuettes of ivory, tortoiseshell, coconut, ostrich egg and amber. On the lowest shelf, cups of turned ivory from the 17th century, attributed to the Zick family of Nüremberg. Most of the other objects were made in Copenhagen c. 1750 by L. Spengler and J.E. Bauert.
818. Figures of ivory and rosewood; made by Simon Troger of Haidhausen, near Munich, in the 18th century.
819. Princess Sophie Hedevig (1677-1735), sister of Frederik IV and founder of Vemmetofte Convent. Half-length, by unknown artist.
820. Peter the Great, the Czar of Russia (1672-1725). Gilt bust of lead. Signed: B.C.D. Rastrelli.
821. Princess Charlotte Amalie (1705-82), daughter of Frederik IV. Half-length, painted by J.S. du Wahl.

Room 9. The Princess's Lacquered Chamber

The tower chamber was originally Christian IV's Golden Chamber, decorated with floral designs on wooden panelling. It was used for confidential discussions when the King held official receptions in the adjoining Audience Chamber (Room 10). During the years 1663-65, Queen Sophie Amalie had the chamber redecorated with chinoiserie in lacquer set with turquoises and mother-of-pearl. The work was done by the Dutch artist Francis de Bray and was based on illustrated Chinese travel accounts and novels, Japanese lacquered boxes and decorative art. The Chamber was restored in 1716 by Christian van Bracht, after which time it was used by Princess Sophie Hedevig, sister of Frederik IV. The chairs, writing and dressing table are examples of lacquered furniture made around 1730 in Canton according to »English« taste. However, two of the chairs are copies made in Copenhagen in the 1750's. The brass chandelier hung with rock crystal is probably French and was rescued from the Sophie Amalienborg fire in 1689.

901. Guitar covered with tortoiseshell and ivory; bears French inscriptions and the monogram of Princess Sophie Hedevig. Made by Joachim Tielke in Hamburg, 1703.
902. Princess Sophie Hedevig. Painting attributed to Jan Frans Douwen.
903. Writing set, of faience, decorated in blue. From the factory in Store Kongensgade. Signed with the mark of J.V. Pfau, and the letter M.
904. Silver jug in the shape of a horse.
905. Firescreen. On the front a Harlequin scene embroidered in wool presumably by Queen Charlotte Amalie and Princess Sophie Hedevig; on the back Frederik IV's monogram worked in silver thread on velvet. Silver tripod and top made by Jean Henri de Moor in Copenhagen, 1690.
907. Flute with a lion and a hart in diamond engraving, with coloured spun glass on the foot. The Netherlands, c. 1680.
908. Memorial Cup commemorating Carl XII. Bohemia or Silesia, 1720's.
909. Covered cup of glass with knop in the shape of a crown. England, c. 1680?
910. Cup with Frederik IV's crowned monogram and 1701. Potsdam.
911. »Triad« with table, guéridons and mirror. Ebony inlaid with flowers, birds and insects in coloured sycamore and bone. Denmark, c. 1680?
912. Two candlesticks of silver plate with varicoloured and clear cut-glass pendants and pearls. Bought in Italy by Frederik IV in 1709.
913. Toilet set of silver with the monogram of Duchess Hedevig Sophie of Holstein-Gottorp, sister of King Carl XII of Sweden. Made in Paris about 1660-75.
914. Octagonal tabletop with embroidered playing cards. Rim of silver. From c. 1700-10. Embroidered by Queen Charlotte Amalie and Princess Sophie Hedevig?
915. Beaker with Görtz coins, made 1724 by Jacob v. Holten.
916. Tea-table of ebony with inlaid sycamore and bone. The Netherlands, c. 1675.
917. A coffee pot of Japanese porcelain with silver mounting in which a crowned F4 can be seen. The spout is formed like the Holstein nettle-leaf.
918. Six cups of Chinese porcelain lined with silver.

Room 10. Frederik IV's Room

The room was originally one bay longer and was used as Christian IV's Audience Chamber. A marble fireplace (now in Room 6) and ceiling paintings with mythological motifs (now in Room 2) belonged to the room's original decorations, and on the walls were family portraits of the King's family. As part of a conversion in 1700, the room was shortened and furnished as an antechamber for Frederik IV's sister, Princess Sophie Hedevig. The painted ceiling panels (originally on the first section of the Long Hall's ceiling and probably painted by Anders Nielsen in 1623) were moved here on the same occasion, and the walls were lined with tapestries woven in Audenarde. The rock crystal chandelier with chiselled steel arms was probably made in Vienna, attributed to Anton Matthias Joseph Domanöck and a present from Empress Marie Theresa. It hung in the King's Audience Chamber at Christiansborg from 1754-94.

1001. Frederik IV: small equestrian silver statuette, presented to the King as a New Year present by Queen Louise in 1701; made in Copenhagen by the King's goldsmith Andreas Normand. The enamelled coats-of-arms by Josias Barbette?

1002. Table with with inlaid semi-precious stones. A present to Frederik IV, 1709, from the Grand Duke of Tuscany.

1003. Cabinet decorated with water-colours of biblical scenes copied from pictures by Raphael; made in Rome c. 1700. At the top, a night-clock with an inside signature: Gio. Wendelinus Hessler fecit Romae. In a drawer, a built-in spinettino dated 1678? Purchased in 1767 for Christiansborg.

1004. Frederik IV as Crown Prince; painted in 1693 by Hyacinthe Rigaud, Paris.

1006. Frederik IV on horseback. Ivory relief. Signed: I(acob) D(obbermann).

1007. Tea service. A teapot, two sugar bowls and cups. Gilded silver with chinoiserie in lacquer. Made by Elias Adam in Augsburg 1708-9. Presumably a present from Frederik IV to his sister, Sophie Hedevig.

1008. Covered tureen of Icelandic obsidian, made by H. Holst 1725 in Copenhagen and ornamented with miniatures of Frederik IV, Anna Sophie, and Carl XII.

1009. Two carafes with silver gilt mounting. C. 1715, Saxony?

1010. Two carafes with the double monograms of Frederik IV and Christian VI and inscriptions. Saxony, c. 1714.

1011. Medicine chest. Belonged to Queen Louise.

1012. Small marble bust, probably of Frederik IV.

1013. Ivory cup, turned by the Swedish General, Magnus Stenbock (1664-1717), who was captured at Tønningen and died in Danish captivity.

1015. Silver cups with covers. Augsburg work. Tournament prize from a party given for Frederik IV in Dresden 1709.

1016. Silver cup, said to have been used in Copenhagen in 1716 by Peter the Great for Danish brandy *(brændevin)*.

1017. Ivory cup; turned by Peter the Great.

1019. Ivory box containing 6 smaller boxes turned by Frederik IV and presented to Christian V as a New Year gift in 1691.

1020. Chinese cup and saucer, with Danish inscription commemorating the Peace of Frederiksborg, 1720.

1021. Frederik IV crowned by the Goddess of Victory. Silver statuette on a pedestal with gilding and green enamel; made on the occasion of the Peace of Frederiksborg, 1720. Signed: Peter Klein.

1022. Painted ivory fan said to have been bought in Italy by Frederik IV and presented to the Queen.

1023. Small Chinese teapot, with Frederik IV's and Queen Anna Sophie's monograms.

1024. Compass made by Peter the Great bearing his portrait.

1025. The Stud Goblet of silver, from Østrup (Fredensborg); presumably made by the goldsmith Johan Kohlmann.

1026. Frederik IV's leather-covered savings-box.

1028. Ivory reliefs with biblical scenes; made by the Norwegian carver Magnus Berg (1666-1739).

1029. Casket with Trinity Ring of ivory, turned by Magnus Stenbock (as no. 1013).

1032. Frederik IV; relief portrait in ivory.

1033. Phial with oil from the anointing of Frederik IV.

1034. Frederik IV as Prince. Enamelled miniature signed: J. Barbette.

1035. Anna Sophie's signet as Duchess of Slesvig, carved in cornelian.

1036. Silver crucifix with gilded ornamentation. According to Italian accounts, it was given to Frederik IV by Maria Maddalena Trenta, whom the King met for the first time in 1692, and for the second time in 1709, when she had retired to a convent.

1037. Queen Anna Sophie's hymnbook.

1038. Silver watch made by Jacob N. Witte in Copenhagen. On the inside, relief portraits of Frederik IV and Anna Sophie.

1039. Pack of cards with pictures in silk patchwork.
1040. The apotheosis of Frederik IV. Ivory relief made by Magnus Berg.
1041. »Water«; a large ornamental vase of silver, bronze, and ivory, from 1730. The last work of Magnus Berg.
1042. Christian V presiding at the Supreme Court, presumably painted in 1697. The picture is hanging in its original place.
1043. Silver fireguard with Christian VI's cipher as Crown Prince. Made in 1723 by Marcus Pipgros in Copenhagen.
1044. Two silver andirons with the Hessian arms and the monogram and arms of the Landgravine Hedewig Sophie, mother of Queen Charlotte Amalie; dated 1654. Made in Cassel by Christoph Bucher.
1045. Grandfather clock with lacquered chinoiserie. The dial is signed: W:m Webster Exchange Alley, London.
1046. Inlaid walnut »secretary« from the 18th century, presumably with the monogram of Christian VI.
1047. Equestrian statuette of Frederik IV, carved in ivory and wood by Simon Troger.
1048. Cabinet, decorated with lacquer and with mosaics of semiprecious stones. Lacquering by Christian van Bracht, mosaics brought back from Florence by Frederik IV in 1709. Belonged to the King's sister, Princess Sophie Hedevig.
1049.-1050. Frederik IV and Queen Louise. Marble busts made by Just Wiedewelt, 1719.
1053. Double portrait of Frederik IV and his sister, Sophie Hedevig; painted on a corrugated surface, so that only one at a time can be seen; executed in 1692 by G.A. Bois-Clair.
1054. Two lacquered tables with mirrors, made by the van Bracht family? Part of the lacquered furnishings made for the King's Chamber (Room 6). 1720s?

Room 11. Frederik IV's Cabinet

The room was used by Frederik IV's sister, Princess Sophie Hedevig, as an Audience Chamber; none of its original furnishings has been preserved. When, in the last century, Rosenborg was arranged in the form of a chronological collection, the first floor was furnished with royal interiors from Frederiksberg Palace or »Prinsens Palæ«, which on the dissolution of Absolutism became the property of the State. The inlaid floor is also from »Prinsens Palæ«.

The left-hand wall is hung with a so-called juice tapestry painted with translucent distemper; a speciality of the Netherlands where it adorned living rooms. On the right-hand wall a Flemish tapestry depicting a harvesting scene from the late 17th century. The faience stove in the corner was made at the Blue Tower factory in the 1740's; Frederik IV's and Anna Sophie's names are to be found on the iron frame from 1729.

1101. Eight chairs of mahogany with carved acanthus backs, seats, later, with mounted gilded leather. Acquired by Christian V for Frederiksborg Palace in the 1690s.
1102. »Triad« with table, guéridons and mirror of boxwood, inlaid with Chinese figures of bone and exotic wood. The set originally also included a cabinet, and stood in the Marble Chamber (Room 5) in 1718.
1103. Clock in the shape of a pyramid, covered with tortoiseshell and ornamented with silverwork; signed by the Augsburg master, J.A. Thelot. The dial is marked: Georg Braun.
1104. Cabinet with drawers and doors decorated in 1707 by Hendrik Krock with amorous scenes.
1105. Nautilus shell mounted as an ornamental cup, made in Copenhagen by Jürgen Kurtz 1697.
1107. Ivory reliefs by Magnus Berg.
1110. Small painting representing Christ escorting Anna Sophie to Heaven, where Frederik IV awaits her.
1111. Hunting scene made of papier-maché by Christian van Bracht.
1112. Princess Sophie Hedevig, daughter of Christian V; three-quarter length, painted by Benoît le Coffre.
1114. Queen Anna Sophie, painted by J.S. du Wahl?
1115. Frederik IV as an old man, painted by Balthasar Denner.
1116. Frederik IV; three-quarter length, painted by J.S. du Wahl.
1117. Queen Louise, consort of Frederik IV; three-quarter length, painted by J.S. du Wahl.

Room 12. Christian VI's Room

The room was originally the bedchamber of Frederik IV's sister, Sophie Hedevig. The walls are now hung with tapestries depicting scenes from the life of Alexander the Great. They were brought as samples by the tapestry-weaver, Bernt van der Eichen, who was summoned from Flanders in 1684 before receiving the order for the tapestries illustrating the war-time feats of Christian V, which were hung in the Long Hall (The Knights' Hall). The parquet floor was moved here c. 1870 from Frederiksberg Palace, from which came the ceiling painting, »Flora Distributing Blessing over Denmark«, painted by Benoît le Coffre. The sofa and six stools from c. 1750 were rescued from the fire of Christiansborg Palace and presumably belonged to Queen Sophie Magdalene.

1201. Queen Sophie Magdalene's lathe designed by D. de Thurah 1735-36.
1202. Ivory bust of Sophie Magdalene; stands in a small temple, and is said to have been made by the Elector Wilhelm I of Hesse-Cassel (1743-1821).
1203. Console clock, signed: Pierre Leroy de la société des arts, one of the most famous watchmakers of France.
1204. Silver gilt toilet set, made in Augsburg, 1743-49, among others, by the masters, J. Martin Satzger, A. Winkler, J. Georg Klosse, J.N. Spickermann. Bought by Christian VIII.
1205. Two lantern clocks with musical works, silver-mounted, from Frederik IV's time. Signed: Claudius du Chesne Londini and: J. Mitchell, London. The silver-mounting of the consoles made in Copenhagen 1738 by J. Schowert.
1207. Sophie Magdalene. Half-length, painted by Andreas Brünniche.
1208. Agate bowl with silver mounting, which includes a modelled figure of Neptune. Presented to Christian VI by the Jews of Altona during a visit by the King. Made about 1735 in Augsburg, by Johannes Biller.
1209. Silver gilt toilet set, with a crowned »L« presumably signifying Queen Louise, born Princess of England, later consort of Frederik V. Made in Augsburg about 1740-45 by Salomon Dreyer, Jacob Lutz, Gottlieb Mentzel, and other masters.
1210. Large cabinet with gilt, carved figures, and rich inlays showing Christian VI's monogram and the various fields of the Danish coat-of-arms. Made in Copenhagen 1732 by Dietrich Schäffer.
1211. Christian VI. Small alabaster bust made by Jens Karleby in 1768.
1213. Christian VI. Half-length, painted by J.S. du Wahl.
1215. Ivory reliefs by Magnus Berg (1666-1739).

1216. Silver model showing the landing-stage in Bergen, on the occasion of Christian VI's visit in 1733. Made by the goldsmith Johannes Müller in Bergen 1734.

1217. Christian VI, full-length portrait, presumably painted by J.S. du Wahl.

1218. Portrait of Princess Charlotte Amalie, daughter of Frederik IV. Signed: P. Wichmann.

1220. Carriage clock of silver with Christian VI's monogram. Made by Peder Nøttestad in Christiania (Oslo) 1740.

1221. Cameo with elephant and cross of dannebrog in table-cut diamonds, carved in jasper by Lorenz Natter in 1744.

1222. A Meissner porcelain plate with the page of an almanac showing the birthdays of Christian VI and Sophie Magdalene.

1223. Miniature cabinet of silver filigree with representations of the regalia. Made by Johannes Müller in Bergen, 1736, in commemoration of Christian VI's and Sophie Magdalene's visit to Norway in 1733.

1224. Silver trowel used by Christian VI when laying the foundation-stone of Christiansborg Palace on 21st April 1733. Later used by Frederik VII when laying the foundation-stone of St. John's Church in Nørrebro on 20th June 1856.

1225. Christian VI with his family; presumably painted by Marcus Tuscher.

1226. Chest of drawers made of walnut with bronze mounting, by C.J. Preisler in Copenhagen about 1740-43.

1227. Sofa and stools. Whitepainted and gilded wood with carving and cartouches with painted motifs. Venice or South Germany c. 1740? Saved from the fire at Christiansborg Palace in 1794.

1228. Two gilt carved armchairs, upholstered with embroidered landscapes and flowers in petit point. Made c. 1745 in Paris or Copenhagen for A.G. Moltke's Palace at Amalienborg.

1229. Silver plate with homage to Christian VI, from »most humble servant Thomes Thomesen« who found the silver himself at his farm in Nedenes Len, Norway. Presented to the King, when visiting Arendal, august 23rd, 1733.

1230. Two labels of parchment with inscription telling about the visit of Queen Sophie Magdalene at the silvermine in Kongsberg, june 30th, 1733. Here the Queen, with her own hand won a piece of silver. The silverpiece has later disappeared.

Room 13. The Antechamber or »The Rose«.
(Frederik V's Room)

The name »The Rose« goes back to the time of Frederik IV, when this central antechamber was used as a dining-room for the ladies and gentlemen of the court. Later the room was used by The Royal Lottery. In the 19th century the room was restored to its original quadratic shape. The fittings, ceiling paintings, gilt leather wall-coverings and parquet floor were taken from Frederiksberg Palace. The ceiling paintings are painted by Frederik IV's court painters, Benoît le Coffre and Hendrik Krock. The chandelier, made in England at the end of the 18th century, originates from Jægerspris Palace. »The Rose« also contains paintings, furniture and curios from the Rococo time of Frederik V.

1300. Painted brown cupboard with gilt carving and glass-lined doors. Originally white. Made for Queen Sophie Magdalene's private cabinet at Christiansborg Palace for storing the valuables.
1301. Portrait of Frederik V as a young man, painted by J.S. du Wahl.
1302. Double portrait of Frederik V and Queen Louise, painted on ivory; by unknown artist.
1303. Faience bust representing King Frederik V. Made after a bust by J. Saly (from 1754), probably at the Østerbro factory in Copenhagen c. 1765.
1304. Ivory carriage, with a lady-in-waiting. Signed: D. de Thurah fecit 1749.
1305. Ivory figure representing Piety and made for the birthday of Frederik V 1761, possibly by Lorenz Spengler.
1306. Faience bust representing Count Adam Gottlob Moltke, Lord High Steward (1710-92). Presumably from the factory in Kastrup.
1307. Princess Louise, Frederik V's sister (1726-56). Duchess of Saxe-Hildburghausen. Three-quarter portrait, signed: T. Huber.
1308. »The Glorification of the Chase«. Made in ivory, lapis lazuli, jasper, etc., by J.E. Bauert and Lorenz Spengler.
1309. Queen Louise, full-length, painted by Pilo.
1310. Walnut commode with gilt carving. Copenhagen, c. 1740. Possibly made by Matthias Orthmann.

1311. Three carved, gilded armchairs marked »C6« and »KSCB 1740«, i.e. from the Royal Palace of Christiansborg, which was inaugurated in 1740.

1312. Frederik V's Queen, Louise, born Princess of England. Full-length, painted by C.G. Pilo.

1313. Prince Frederik. Small full-length painting by J.G. Ziesenis 1767.

1314. Portrait of Princess Louise, sister of Frederik V; by unknown artist.

1315. Statuette of ivory representing Diana with a hound; presumably made by Lorenz Spengler.

1316. Margrave Friedrich Ernst of Brandenburg-Baireuth (1703-62); Queen Sophie Magdalene's brother, Governor of Schleswig and Holstein, Danish Field-Marshal, Lieutenant General. Small three-quarter portrait on copper, signed: J.F. Gerhard fec.

1317. Portrait of Frederik V as a young man by J.S. du Wahl.

1318. Frederik V. Painted terra cotta relief by L. von Lücke. c. 1753.

1320. Queen Louise. Painting from the studio of C.G. Pilo.

1321. Frederik V. Equestrian picture; allegorical representation, signed: J.F. Gerhard 1747.

1322. Cabinet in walnut veneer with inlays of landscapes in semiprecious stones. Made in c. 1740 for Hirschholm Palace.

1323. A pair of potpourri vases with hunting scenes, made at the Royal Copenhagen Porcelain Manufactory in 1780 for the Dowager Queen Juliane Marie.

1328. Gilded, carved console table with top of black marble. Marked »C6« and »KSCB«, i. e. from Christiansborg Palace, which was inaugurated in 1740.

1329. Portrait of Frederik V as a young man; painted by J.S. du Wahl.

1330. Rosewood cabinet with inlays of coloured bone, mother-of-pearl, and metal. In the drawer a spinette. Made in Copenhagen 1755 by C.F. Lehmann.

1331. Queen Juliane Marie; copy, after C.G. Pilo.

1332. Princess Sophie Magdalene (1746-1813), Frederik V's daughter, Queen of Sweden. Pastel, by Lorents Pasch.

1333. Frederik V; relief portrait in biscuit, by L. Fournier.

1334. Portrait of the Landgravine Louise of Hesse, daughter of Frederik V. Copy after C.B. Perronneau.

1335. Two console cabinets of walnut with gilt carving; originally mirrors on the upper cabinet doors. Bookcases saved from the Christiansborg Palace fire in 1794. Denmark, c. 1750.

1336. Post rider carved in ivory by Jørgen Garnaas for Frederik V.

1337. Ivory temple. Signed: (crowned) J.M. (viz: Juliane Marie) fecit. Ao. 1754.

1338. Turned ivory vase. Signed: L. Spengler Tourneur de S. M. le Roy, 1752.

1339. Equestrian statuette of ivory: the Emperor Paul of Russia (1754-1801) as Grand Duke. Made by C.A. von Lücke.

1340. Walnut cabinet with flute-work and music cylinder. Made by C.F. Lehmann in Copenhagen, finished 1757.

1342.-1343. Two ivory cups; signed by Christian VII's cousins and future brothers-in-law, respectively Wilhelm and Carl, Princes of Hesse, 1759.

1344. Various specimens of the oldest Danish porcelain, pâte tendre; made in Copenhagen by L. Fournier c. 1765.

1345. Centre piece representing a double portal, of ivory, ebony and tortoiseshell; with bust of Frederik V. Made on the occasion of the centenary of the introduction of Absolutism and signed: L. Spengler d. 16 october 1760.

1346. Duke Ernst Friedrich Carl of Saxe-Hildburghausen (1727-80), brother-in-law of Frederik V. Three-quarter portrait, signed: T. Huber 1751.

1347. Frederik V; miniature painted on porcelain, signed: I. Gylding pinxit.

1348. Juliane Marie; relief in biscuit, signed: Bauert.

1349. Duke Carl of Brunswick (1713-80). Relief in biscuit.

1350. The Elector Friedrich August II of Saxony, King of Poland (1696-1763); painted on porcelain, signed: I. Gylding pinxit.

1351. Crown cup from the Norwegian glass factory at Nøstetangen. Richly engraved with Frederik V's monogram. Signed: H.G. Köhler 1752.

1352.-1353. Cups of Norwegian glass, engraved on the occasion of the coronation of Frederik V, 1747, by H.G. Köhler.

1354. Crown cup of Norwegian glass, with the monogram of Christian VII and Caroline Mathilde, and the date MDCCLXVI, 8th (Nov., i. e. the wedding day). Engraved by H.G. Köhler.

1355. Frederik V, relief in porcelain; made by L. Fournier.

1356. White clock, with carved gilded Rococo ornaments, and flute-work. Signed: I.P. Adamy in Stettin.

1357. War game »Romans and Africans«. A total of 250 silver gilt figurines made for Frederik V as Crown Prince and King. 109 of the figures supplied by Christopher II Fabritius as a supplement to an earlier set of chessmen, made in Augsburg c. 1700 and given to Princess Sophie Hedevig by Frederik IV.

The Mirror Cabinet

Furnished for Frederik IV c. 1700 and modelled on the Versailles of the Sun King. In several places during Baroque times a mirror cabinet was incorporated in the King's suite as its innermost and most intimate room, often in connection with the bedchamber. Frederik IV's bedchamber was on the ground floor (Room 4), with access to the mirror cabinet via the spiral staircase of the tower. Visitors saw themselves reflected in both ceiling, walls and oval floor; the latter may have constituted a problem for female visitors wearing the fish-bone skirts of that time but it was scarcely an accident. In the adjacent room there was a »resting bench«, and Frederik IV kept his collection of erotica in the wall-cabinet.

1390. Clock in ivory case with gilded ornaments and precious stones, and bearing Frederik V's signature. Signed: I. Hein. Klein Copenhagen.
1391. Spinette signed by the instrument maker C.F. Speer, who was paid regularly for tuning the royal children's instrument. It belonged to Frederik V's daughter, Princess Louise.
1392. Three covered cups of glass with knop in the form of a crown. Made at the glass factory at Nøstetangen, c. 1750.
1393. Two cabinets with inlaid Italian mosaics. Frames and stands Danish work, mosaics brought back from Florence by Frederik IV in 1709. Belonged to the King's daughter, Princess Charlotte Amalie.
1394. Model of a ship of the line in tortoiseshell, mother-of-pearl and amber. Made by Customs officer Niels Nielsen in Ålborg in 1760.
1395. Christian VI, terra cotta bust, by unknown artist.
1396. Frederik V, terra cotta bust.

Room 14. Frederik V's Cabinet

This is the first of the rooms occupied by Frederik IV's brother, Prince Carl. The walls are hung with tapestries from Charles le Vigne's factory in Berlin representing garden scenes from the beginning of the 18th century. The sofa and the two armchairs from c.

1750 presumably originate from Fredensborg Palace, while the commode, in rosewood veneer, was possibly made at the studio of C.F.Lehmann. The porcelain was largely rescued from the fire of Christiansborg in 1794.

1401. »Science and Art Paying Homage to Frederik V«. Sketch signed: Peder Als inv. et pinx.
1402. Queen Juliane Marie, bust in biscuitware, signed: Luplau fec. 1781, and made at the Royal Copenhagen Porcelain Manufactory. After a model by C.F. Stanley? The Queen ardently patronized the Manufactory during its first years.
1403. Portrait of Frederik V in his coronation robes. Half-length painting by C.G. Pilo.
1404. The Heir Presumptive, Prince Frederik. Biscuit statuette made in 1791 by A. Hald, after the model by L. Grossi. The Royal Copenhagen Porcelain Manufactory.
1405. Two vases of Royal Copenhagen Porcelain with relief portraits of Juliane Marie and of Prince Frederik, c. 1780.
1406. Two vases of Royal Copenhagen Porcelain with portraits of Juliane Marie and Prince Frederik. C. 1784-86.
1407. Painted commode of wood, brown, originally blue, with fire-gilt bronzes representing i.a. sculpture, painting, music and architecture. Made for Fredensborg Palace c. 1765. Possibly designed by N.H. Jardin.
1408. Rod, with heights of Frederik V's children.
1409. Gustav III of Sweden with his family. Etching by F.J. Martin, probably after Cornelius Høyer.
1410. Prince Ferdinand of Brunswick (1721-92), brother of Queen Juliane Marie, Prussian Fieldmarshal. Relief in biscuit. Royal Copenhagen Porcelain, c. 1781.
1411. Bird cage of bronze gilt with clock, musical works, and movable birds. Paris, c. 1780. Hung in Queen Marie Sophie Frederikke's Audience Chamber at Christiansborg Palace.
1412. Christian VII. Enamelled miniature by G. Seiptius c. 1783.
1413. Christian VII; enamelled miniature, signed: C.F. Schrader.
1414. Queen Juliane Marie's big travelling-clock, signed: Mathias Schreiner. Friedberg.
1415. Queen Juliane Marie as a young woman. Enamelled miniature, possibly by J. Brecheisen.
1416. Frederik, the Heir Presumptive, as a seven-year-old. Enamelled miniature, signed: Brecheisen J. Copenhagen 1760.
1417. Frederik V. Relief in biscuit, made by L. Fournier, c. 1765.
1418. Gold watch signed: Murray, London.
1419. William Augustus, Duke of Cumberland. Made by Z.F. Zincke?

1420. Queen Caroline Mathilde's sister, Princess Marie (married 1740 to Landgrave Frederik II of Hesse-Cassel). Enamelled miniature, by unknown artist.

1421. The Empress Catharine II of Russia (1729-96). Enamelled miniature by Vigilius Erichsen c. 1755?

1422. Count Adam Gottlob Moltke (1710-98), painted on porcelain. Signed: J. Gylding pinxit 1763.

1423. Rod, bearing the measurements of the heights of Prince Frederik's children.

1424. Princess Sophie Frederikke (1758-94) (née Princess of Mecklenburg-Schwerin), painted by J.C.F. Viertel.

1425. Christian VII. Portrait en grisaille, after Jens Juel; painted on porcelain. Royal Copenhagen Porcelain, c. 1785.

1426. Portrait of Queen Caroline Mathilde when young, oil on copper; possibly after F. Coates.

1427. Caroline Mathilde, painted by C. Sparkjær.

1428. Caroline Mathilde, by unknown artist.

1429. Christ and the Apostles. Porcelain paintings, signed: J. Gylding pinx 1764: set in a gilt metal frame.

1430. Prince Frederik, the Heir Presumptive. Ivory figure; baby in swaddling clothes (1753). Signed: L. von Lücke fecit.

1431. Enamelled box, with picture of Copenhagen harbour in the lid, c. 1750.

1432. Two enamelled boxes with child portraits of Frederik, the Heir Presumptive, and Christian VII; made by J. Brecheisen c. 1760.

1433. Two enamelled dressing cases, set in gold, with portraits of Frederik V and Juliane Marie. Made by Jørgen Gylding?

1434. Enamelled box with picture of King Friedrich II of Prussia (1712-86). Half-length after Pesne, signed: Brecheisen, 1757.

1435. Chessboard with amber chessmen. Made by Lorenz Spengler, c. 1750.

1436. Amber chandelier made by Lorenz Spengler after design by Marcus Tuscher.

1437. Enamelled box with Frederik V's portrait and allegories of the Fine Arts. Joseph Brecheisen, 1760.

1438. Box with allegories, Juliane Marie's monogram and the inscriptions: Forever, and: For the Best Queen. Made for her birthday, 4.9.1781, at the Royal Copenhagen Porcelain Manufactory.

1439. Writing table of carved gilt wood. Made c. 1740 in Copenhagen from a design by L.-A. Le Clerc?

Room 15. Christian VII's Room

This room, together with Rooms 14 and 16, was designed 1782-84 as a cabinet for the Royal Coin Collection after a drawing by Johannes Wiedewelt. The panels and portals, amongst other things, originate from this time, so the room forms an appropriate setting for the collections from Christian VII's time. The latter time is remembered in particular for the great agrarian reforms carried out while the Crown Prince, later King Frederik VI, acted from 1784 as regent for his sick father. The exhibits show the influence of late 18th century neo-classicism both French (Louis XVI) and English.

1500. Mahogany escritoire with intarsia, Denmark c. 1800. Was originally at Frederiksberg Palace, possibly as part of the new furnishings for Frederik VI after his wedding in 1790.
1501. Frederik VI as a child. Pastel by H.P. Sturz, 1771, (Queen Caroline Mathilde's confidant).
1502. Princess Louise Augusta as a child. Pastel by H.P. Sturz, 1771.
1503. Punchbowl of Royal Copenhagen Porcelain depicting the Battle of Copenhagen, 2nd April, 1801. One of the 44 examples Count Roepstorff had made as presents for the officers who took part.
1504. Two vase candelabras delivered in 1790 to Christiansborg. After the palace fire of 1794 they were placed on the two guéridons procured 1794-95 for Christian VII's palace at Amalienborg. The candelabras and the guéridons were delivered by C.J. Lillie.
1505. Christian VII; oval, painted by Jens Juel.
1506. Frederik VI when prince; oval, painted by Jens Juel.
1507. Caroline Mathilde. Oval, after Jens Juel, 1771.
1508. Gilded armchair with shield-shaped back. Purchased 1790 for the Crown Prince Frederik (VI) at Christiansborg.
1509. Crown Prince Frederik as a three-year-old. Wax bust by J.E. Bauert 1771.
1510. The Crown Prince's playmate, Carl. Wax bust by J.E. Bauert.
1511. Christian VII: three-quarter length, by Jens Juel.
1512. Frederik VI, oval painted by Jens Juel about 1784.
1513. Caroline Mathilde, oval, by Peder Als, c. 1767.
1514. Princess Louise Augusta, sister of Frederik VI, Duchess of Augustenborg. Oval, painted by Jens Juel about 1785.

1515. Gilded armchair with oval back. Made c. 1780. Designed by the architect G.E. Rosenberg.

1516. Princess Marie Louise (1792-1793), painted by Jens Juel.

1517. Cabinet of rosewood and walnut, with inlays of mother-of-pearl and coloured bone. Used for coins and bears Queen Juliane Marie's monogram in bronze.

1518. Oval mahogany table with silver plate; the plate executed by the Court Goldsmith, Nicolai Jensen Lyderwahl 1796.

1519. Frederik VI as Prince in admiral's uniform, oval. Copy; presumably painted by Hans Hansen after Jens Juel.

1520. Queen Marie Sophie Frederikke, with the Order of Christian VII: painted by Jens Juel.

1521. Queen Caroline Mathilde, painted after her death by Jens Juel.

1522. Mahogany dressing-table, inlaid with flowers and figures in coloured wood and furnished with mechanical appliances. Signed: Made in the year 1793 and repaired 1816. Master-joiner I. Pengel (Copenhagen). The inlay on the top made by David Roentgen.

1523. Frederik VI as Crown Prince and Marie Sophie Frederikke. Silhouettes, painted by Rothermundt.

1524. Man-of-war made by Danish prisoners of war in England after 1807, from the bones left on their plates; acquired by Frederik VI in 1810.

1525. Grand Cross of the Greek Order of Our Saviour; presented to Christian VIII by King Otto of Greece.

1526. Norwegian chamberlain's keys from 1814.

1527. Grand Cross of the Spanish Marie Louise Order.

1528-1532; Frederik VI's Foreign Decorations: *1528.* Star and Chain of the French Order of the Holy Ghost. – *1529.* The Insignia and Star of the Order of the Westphalian Crown. – *1530.* Star and Insignia of the Order of the Dutch Union. – *1531.* Star and Insignia of the French Legion of Honour (from the time of Napoleon). – *1532.* Star and Insignia of the French Legion of Honour (after the fall of Napoleon).

1533. Christian VIII's Grand Cross of the Legion of Honour, Insignia and Star from the period of King Louis Philippe.

1534. Prince Frederik, the Heir Presumptive. Biscuit bust after model by Hartmann Beeken; made at the Royal Copenhagen Porcelain Manufactory.

1535. Set of mirrors consisting of gilded, carved pier glass delivered, 1785, to the Audience Chamber of Frederik, the Heir Presumptive, at Frederiksberg. Also gilded, carved console procured, 1778, for Queen Juliane Marie's brother, Duke Carl of Brunswick-Bevern, at Fredensborg Palace.

1536. Tea service of Royal Copenhagen Porcelain, with Princess

Sophie Frederikke's monogram and dated 24th August 1783 (i. e. the Princess's 25th birthday).

1537. Frederik VI's cup and saucer of porcelain, with the King's portrait and monogram in gold. The Royal Copenhagen Porcelain Manufactory.

1538. Frederik VI's travelling-watch; in silver case, signed: J.H. Müller, Schleswig.

1539. Knitting-bag. On the lock, a gold medal made on the occasion of the wedding of Prince Frederik, later Frederik VII, and Princess Vilhelmine 1828 by C. Jørgensen.

1540. Miniature edition of the Right of Citizenship Act; in silver binding with a crowned F. 1776.

1542. Gold locket with a few drops of the anointing oil. 31. July, 1815.

1543. Gold signet ring with portrait of Frederik VI.

1546. Rings made of the Landgrave Carl of Hesse's metal, which was intended to render gold and silver superfluous.

1547. Lime hod and trowel of silver used by Frederik VI when laying the foundationstone of Vonsild Church in South Jutland, 1824.

1548. Paperweight with profile portrait of Frederik VI as an old man.

1549. Medal with Frederik VI's portrait, by C. Christensen; stamped by the City of Copenhagen on the occasion of the King's recovery, 1833.

1550. Box and other articles of the Landgrave Carl's metal (see no. 1546), with Frederik VI's and Queen Marie's monogram.

1551. Portrait of Queen Marie Sophie Frederikke, cut in chalcedony by A. Jacobson; also an impression of the stone.

1552. Plaster of Paris impression of medal with Frederik VI's portrait 1834, modelled by F.C. Krohn, for the 50 years' jubilee.

1553. Frederik VI. Relief in gilt bronze, made by Leopold Heuberger during the Congress of Vienna, 1814.

1554. Semi-circular dressing-table of light mahogany with intarsia. On the top, the Danish coat-of-arms. Masterpiece by Jens Brøtterup, 1784.

1555. Queen Caroline Mathilde; pastel by Jens Juel.

1556. Christian VII: pastel by unknown artist.

1557. Prince Frederik, the Heir Presumptive, brother of Christian VII, father of Christian VIII, after Jens Juel.

1558. Queen Caroline Mathilde; full-length with Prince Frederik (VI) on her lap. Gouache, painted in 1771 by Andreas Thornborg and sent to the Court with a plea for support (no. 1501).

1559. The six-year-old Crown Prince Frederik (VI) depicted as the

1605. Princess Louise Augusta. Full-length, painted 1791 by Anton Graff.

1609. Chair of gilt carved wood with velvet covering. Made for Princess Caroline Amalie's throne-room in Christian VIII's Palace c. 1830. Designed by G.F. Hetsch?

1610. Frederik VI in his coronation robes. Sketch by Vilhelm Bendz, 1830.

1611. Frederik VI; statuette in bronzed plaster of Paris, c. 1810.

1612. Frederik VI in the uniform of the Life Guards; painted by C.W. Eckersberg, 1826.

1613.-1614. Ferdinand, the Heir Presumptive, and Princess Caroline. Watercolours by L. Grünbaum, 1829.
Patron of Science with Minerva in the background. Unsigned, copy after Peder Brünniche, 1774.

1560. Table with green covering used by King Frederik VI in Council. From Amalienborg; made by the cabinet-maker Hans Babe, 1803.

1561. Small carved iron box with gold inlay (the Danish coat-of-arms). Inside is a miniature rifle, signed: J. Löbnitz.

1562. Case for Frederik VI's water-bottle.

1563. Frederik VI's telescope.

1564. Frederik VI's field pocket-book, and a manoeuvre map of the environs of Copenhagen c. 1805.

1565. Frederik VI's compasses for the manoeuvre maps; made in Copenhagen in 1795 by J.F.B. Oppen.

1566. Frederik VI's pedometer.

Room 16. Frederik VI's Room

Like the two previous ones, this narrow room is one of the interiors designed by Wiedewelt, 1782-84. The devastating war with England during the reign of Frederik VI led to Denmark's separation from Norway in 1814. But the period of economic difficulty following upon the State bankruptcy in 1813 became at the same time the Golden Age in Danish literature and art. The furniture and handicraft is influenced by the so-called Empire style.

1601. Princess Vilhelmine, daughter of Frederik VI; full-length, painted by L. Aumont, 1831.

1602.-1603. Frederik VI and Queen Marie Sophie Frederikke; medallions by Plötz, Jun. 1822, after busts by Thorvaldsen.

1604. Child's chair; used by Frederik VI as a child.

1615. Frederik VI as Prince, about 1805. Full-length, presumably painted by W. Haffner.
1616. Frederik VI walking with his family in Frederiksberg Gardens, about 1813. Watercolour by J. Senn.
1617. Frederik VI's desk from Amalienborg.
1618. Frederik VI's tumbler.
1619. Frederik VI with Queen Marie Sophie Frederikke and the Princesses Caroline and Wilhelmine; painted by C.W. Eckersberg, 1821.
1622. Queen Marie Sophie Frederikke, drawn in 1810 by J.P. (?) Møller after painting by Jens Juel.
1623. Two chairs used at Augustenborg for Christian VIII's wedding, 1815.
1624. Frederik VI's telescope, later used by Frederik VII. Signed: J. Bidstrup, London.
1625. Clock, of gilt bronze, with equestrian statuette of Frederik VI. The statuette attributed to F.C. Krohn.
1626. Turkish scimitar, with gold hilt and sheath. A present to Frederik VI from the Queen of Akim (in Ghana) who in 1824-26, as Denmark's ally, vanquished the King of Ashanti and seized his treasures.
1627. Tobacco pipe of gold, presented by the same Queen to a Danish general.
1628. Cup and saucer of French porcelain, with a »Charlotte«, and a crowned »Friederich«, respectively.
1629. Cup and saucer, with portrait of Frederik VII when young. The model was designed in 1824 by G.F. Hetsch. The Royal Copenhagen Porcelain Manufactory.
1630. Standish of Royal Copenhagen Porcelain, from 1790.
1631-1635. Five cups and saucers, with portraits of famous Danish men: *1631.* Jonas Collin, government official (1776-1861). – *1632.* A.S. Ørsted, lawyer and statesman (1778-1860). – *1633.* J.P. Mynster, Bishop of Zealand, (1775-1854). – *1634.* Dean H.G. Clausen (1759-1840). – *1635.* Duke Vilhelm of Glücksburg (1786-1831), Christian IX's father. The Royal Copenhagen Porcelain Manufactory.
1636. Three plates of Royal Copenhagen Porcelain; one flowered, two with views, all three with borders, designed by G.F. Hetsch. The flowered plate was made for the dowry of Frederik VI's daughters 1828-29. The other two were part of Frederik VI's dessert service at Christiansborg Palace, 1834.
1637. Princess Caroline; three-quarter length portrait by L. Aumont, 1830.
1638. Frederik VI driving across Kongens Nytorv by torchlight, 1820: painted by C.A. Lorenzen.
1639. Throne of carved white painted and gilded wood, with velvet covering. Designed in 1812 by C.F. Hansen, and used by

Princess Caroline in her Audience Chamber in Bernstorff's Palace.

Room 17. Christian VIII's Room

This gable room facing south-east, together with the adjacent Room 18, acquired its form and its panels when Frederik IV converted Rosenborg's 2nd floor at the beginning of the 18th century. The ceiling is part of the old ceiling in Christian IV's time (as in Room 10). Today the room contains pictures and curios from Christian VIII's time, the final years of Absolutism. However, several objects originate from the King's youth, including the short period when he was King of Norway in 1814. The furniture in particular is influenced by middle-class late classicism.

1701. Christian VIII; painted by W.N. Marstrand 1843.
1702. Queen Caroline Amalie, painted by H. C. Jensen 1879.
1703. Christian VIII. Drawing by Mlle Romili.
1705. Queen Caroline Amalie. Drawing by Mlle Romili.
1706. Christian VIII. Full-length, painted 1831 by L. Aumont.
1707. Christian VIII. Half-length, from c. 1812. Painted by C.G.Kratzenstein-Stub?
1708. Queen Caroline Amalie, Princess of Augustenborg. Signed: L. Aumont 1830.
1709. The Landgrave Vilhelm of Hesse-Cassel (1787-1867), married to Christian VIII's sister, Princess Louise Charlotte, Danish general and Governor of Copenhagen. Signed: C.A. Jensen, Petersburg, 1844.
1710. Christian VIII. Pastel, signed: (C.) Horneman 1810.
1711. Queen Caroline Amalie. Marble bust, made by F.C. Stramboe,1870.
1712. Mahogany writing table with gilded bronze fittings from Christian VIII's study at Amalienborg. See the above drawing in which the King stands in front of his desk. Drawing signed: Chr. Hetsch 1881.
1713. The coronation of Christian VIII. Drawing by I.V. Gertner.
1714. The coronation procession of Christian VIII across the courtyard of Frederiksborg Palace, 28th June 1840, painted by I.V. Gertner.
1715. Christian VIII. Equestrian statuette of silver, made by Adelgunde Herbst.

1716. Jewel box of porcelain plates with flower paintings by I.L. Jensen. A gift from Christian VIII to Queen Caroline Amalie 1842.

1717. Workbox made of sandalwood in India. Belonged to Caroline Amalie.

1718. Queen Caroline Amalie. Drawing from the anointing of the Queen; by I.V. Gertner.

1719. The anointing of Christian VIII in the chapel of Frederiksborg Palace, 28th June 1840. Painted by I.V. Gertner.

1720. Christian VIII. Marble bust, made by F.C. Stramboe.

1721. Queen Caroline Amalie, painted by F.C. Grøger.

1722. Charlotte Frederikke. Christian VIII's first wife and Frederik VII's mother. By unknown artist.

1724. Silver jewel box, French work; presented to Queen Caroline Amalie by Mr. Donner, titular Councillor, Altona.

1726. Princess Charlotte, Frederik VII's mother; painted by F.C. Grøger.

1727. Mantelpiece clock with bronze statuette of Christian VIII. Signed: A. & W. Jacobsen.

1728. Writing desk of walnut, inlaid with coloured bone, mother-of-pearl, and metal. Made by Mathias Christian Preisler c. 1780. Belonged to Queen Caroline Amalie.

1729. Necklace of gold with blue enamel. On the clasp, Princess Charlotte Frederikke's monogram.

1730. Intaglio portraits of Christian VIII and Caroline Amalie, signed: Settari.

1731. Christian VIII's seal and Norwegian bank note, 1814.

1732. Gold seal with cornelian plate; in the coat-of-arms the Norwegian Lion is seen in the top field. Used by Christian VIII as King of Norway 1814.

1733. Clock with enamel, made in Hanau and presented, in 1794, to the eight-year-old Christian (VIII).

1734. Child's spoon of silver gilt and silver tablespoon (master: A. Michelsen); used by Christian VIII for medicine.

1735. Christian VIII. Watercolour by C.E. Sonne, after coronation picture by Eckersberg.

1736. Double portrait of Christian VIII and Caroline Amalie, enthroned and wearing coronation robes. Sketch for J.D. Court's large painting, now at Amalienborg, 1841-42.

1737. Breakfast service of Vienna porcelain. Wedding gift, 1815, from Caroline Amalie to Christian VIII.

1738. Sofa with mahogany carving. Made for Christiansborg Palace, c. 1840.

1739. Two mahogany armchairs with gilded carving. Belonged to Landgrave Vilhelm of Hesse, North Germany, c. 1820.

Room 18. Frederik VII's Room

When the museum was converted into its present form during the last century it attracted international attention. Five years after Frederik VII's death in 1863 a room was furnished for the King. Part of the ceiling from Christian IV's time is also to be found in this room. The velvet wall-coverings were purchased in Venice 1728 for Copenhagen Castle and transferred to Rosenborg in the 1750's. Furniture and pictures, etc. relate of the period between the Schleswig wars and illustrate the tendency to revive the styles of bygone ages.

1801. Frederik VII as a young man, signed: (C.A.) Jensen 1824.
1802. Princess Caroline (1793-1881), daughter of Frederik VII, consort of Prince Ferdinand, the Heir Presumptive. Signed: A. Schiött, 1854.
1803. Prince Frederik (VII)'s and Princess Mariane's wedding procession in Copenhagen 22nd June 1841. Signed: C. Balsgaard 1843.
1804. Frederik VII. Biscuit bust, after H.V. Bissen.
1805. Princess Mariane arriving in the Roads of Copenhagen, 22nd June 1841, on board the warship »Christian VII«. Signed: A. Melbye, Copenhagen 1844.
1806. Portrait of Frederik VII as Prince; by unknown artist.
1807.-1808. Two portraits of Frederik VII as a boy. Pastels by C. Hornemann.
1809. Frederik VII's couch: mahogany, with red Morocco leather covering.
1811. Frederik VII; three-quarter length, signed: I. Vilhelm Gertner, pinx. 1861.
1812. Frederik VII as Crown Prince. Profile drawing, signed: I. Vilhelm Gertner fec. 1841.
1813. Princess Mariane's seal, with the coats-of-arms of Denmark and Mecklenburg, carved in a smoky topaz.
1814. The pen with which Frederik VII signed the Constitution on 5th June, 1849.
1815. Gold watch, made by Carl Edward Schiötz, presented to Jens Hoff, the riding-master, by Frederik VII.
1816. Commemoration medal for Norwegian and Swedish volunteers in the war, 1848.
1817. The Freemasons' medal commemorating the death of Frederik VII.

1818. A lock of Frederik VII's hair; from his death-bed.
1820. The engagement ring of Frederik VII: bears the inscription: 28th May 1826. Vilh. Marie. Prs. of Denm.
1821. The engagement ring of Princess Vilhelmine; bears the inscription: 28th of May 1826, Fr. Carl Chr., Pr. of Denm.
1822. Gold ring with the inscription: Caroline 4th December 1840. Worn by Frederik VII as Prince when he was betrothed to Princess Caroline Charlotte Mariane of Mecklenburg-Strelitz.
1823. Enamelled gold ring, engraved with the letter M; supposed to have belonged to Princess Mariane.
1824. Princess Charlotte, Frederik VII's mother. Silhouette.
1825. Mahogany folding table; bought 1781 for Crown Prince Frederik (VI's) bedroom at Fredensborg Palace.
1826. Two porcelain vases with Frederik VII's portrait. A present from the King to his friend Carl Berling.
1827. Frederik VII as Prince. By unknown artist.
1828. Frederik VII. Drawing, signed: W. Heuer 1825.
1829. The Landgrave Carl of Hesse, drawn by Frederik VII, 1833.
1830. Frederik VII's arm-chair with leaf/drawing board?.
1831. Two large Sèvres vases presented to Frederik VII by the Emperor Napoleon III.
1832. Frederik VII as a child. Painting signed: Kratzenstein Stub 1813.
1833. Frederik VII's speaking-trumpet, of German silver.
1834. Frederik VII as a child. Modelled by Bertel Thorvaldsen 1820, carved in marble 1825.
1835.-1855. Orders and Decorations of Frederik VII. *1835.* Grand Cross and Insignia of the French Legion of Honour. – *1836.* Grand Cross and Insignia of the Hanoverian Order of St. George. – *1837.* Grand Cross of the Sicilian St. Januarii Order. – *1838.* Grand Cross and Insignia of the Military William Order of the Netherlands. – *1839.* Grand Cross of the Italian Annunziata Order. – *1840.* Grand Cross and Insignia of the Hanoverian Order of Guelph. – *1841.* Grand Cross and Insignia of the Belgian Leopold Order. – *1842.* Insignia of the Norwegian Order of St. Olaf. – *1843.* Insignia of the Swedish Order of Seraphim. – *1844.* Grand Cross of the Prussian Order of the Black Eagle. – *1845.* Grand Cross of the Russian Order of St. Andreas. – *1846.* Insignia of the Russian Order of Alexander Nevsky. – *1847* Insignia of the Russian Order of St. Anna. – *1848.* Collar, Insignia, and Star of the Russian Order of the White Eagle. – *1849.* Austro-Hungarian Order of St. Stephen. – *1850-52.* Grand Cross, Star, and Officer's Cross of the French Legion of Honour; found among the ruins of Frederiksborg Palace after the fire

in 1859. – *1853*. Insignia of the Swedish Order of the Sword. – *1854*. Collar and Insignia of the Swedish Vasa Order. – *1855*. Frederik VII's Order of the Freemasons.

1856. Frederik VII as a child. Silver-pencil drawing, signed: Heuer del. 1810.
1857. Frederik VII as a child, half-length. By unknown artist.
1858. Frederik VII's fishing-rod.
1859. Frederik VII in admiral's uniform, painted by H.A.G. Schiött c. 1850.
1861. Frederik VII's desk; a present from King Frederik Wilhelm IV of Prussia.
1862. Countess Danner, Frederik VII's morganatic wife, coloured photograph.
1863. The frigate »Sjælland«. Model, carved in wood.
1864. Princess Charlotte, mother of Frederik VII, Princess of Mecklenburg-Schwerin (1784-1840). Photograph of drawing.
1865. Prince Frederik Ferdinand, the Heir Presumptive (1792-1863), uncle and brother-in-law of Frederik VII. Signed: A. Schiött. 1853.
1866. Prince Frederik (VII)'s and Princess Mariane's wedding procession in Copenhagen, 22nd June 1841. Signed: C. Balsgaard 1845.
1867. Frederik VII as a child, signed: F.C. Grøger 1814.

Room 19. Corridor

The corridor contains furniture and paintings from the time of Christian VII and Frederik VI. The two sets of mirrors are respectively in Rococo style and inspired by French-influenced neo-classicism (Louis XVI).

1900. Frederik V's equestrian statue at Amalienborg. Painting on glass from c. 1820.
1901. Bust in terra cotta, modelled 1773 by Hartmann Beeken. Probably Christine, daughter of the architect C.F. Harsdorff.
1904. Prince Ferdinand of Brunswick; three-quarter length oval, after Johann Georg Ziesenis.
1906. Mahogany commode with gilt carving and grey marble top. Altona, c. 1780.
1908. Frederik the Heir Presumptive (1753-1805), Frederik V's son. Small plaster of Paris bust, presumably by Hartman Beeken.

1909. Console table of carved, gilded wood with white marble top. From c. 1765. Designed by N.H. Jardin?

1910. Two flower pieces in watercolour, signed: Louise Augusta, pinxit 1784.

1912. Frederik VI lying in state, painted by S.P.L. Schack.

1913. Frederik VI's funeral procession to Roskilde Cathedral, painted by H. Hammer.

1914. Frederik VII's red fez.

1915. Frederik VII's pipe, marked: Madera Touren 46.

1916. Frederik VII's fishing tackle; floats were originally pomanders.

1917. Christian VII; painting by unknown artist.

1918. Hall at Christiansborg Palace; Crown Prince Frederik in the foreground; Indian ink drawing, signed: Fecit Wilhelm Haffner 1781.

1919. »The Audience Chamber of His Royal Highness Crown Prince Friedrich« at Christiansborg. Drawing in Indian ink by W. Haffner 1781.

1920. Queen Caroline Mathilde, painted by Jens Juel.

1921. Count J.F. Struensee; copy by Hans Hansen after J. Juel.

1922. Portrait of Duke Frederik Christian (II) of Schleswig and Holstein and Sønderborg-Augustenborg (1765-1814); by unknown artist.

1923. Portrait of Louise Augusta, Frederik VI's sister, married to Duke Frederik Christian (II). By unknown artist.

1924. Juliane Marie. Pastel after Vigilius Erichsen.

1925. Frederik V. Oval pastel, painted by Cornelius Høyer?

1926. Queen Juliane Marie. Oval pastel, painted by Cornelius Høyer?

1927. Prince Frederik, the Heir Presumptive. Oval pastel, painted by Vigilius Erichsen.

1928. Portrait of Prince Frederik, the Heir Presumptive; oval half-length painting by unknown artist.

1929. Prince Frederik, the Heir Presumptive, oval half-length painting by unknown artist; from 1802-06.

1930. Frederik VI. Signed: Drawn and embroidered by Elisabeth Hansen for the 18th October 1820.

Room 20. The Bronze Room

Two gilded bronze sets from the 1820's are exhibited here. They were used as table decorations at large banquets, a custom that originated from the Imperial Court of Napoleon I. One set was ordered by Prince Christian (VIII); the other was a wedding present from Frederik VI to his daughter Caroline and Ferdinand the Heir Presumptive, Christian VIII's brother. A third set, now at Glücksborg, was a wedding present from Frederik VI to Caroline's sister Vilhelmine and Prince Frederik (VII). The first two sets and the decoration of the room in Empire style were donated by the brewer Carl Jacobsen, 1881. Christian VIII's set is still used at State banquets.

2001. Table decoration of gilded bronze, made according to Christian VIII's instructions during his journey abroad, 1819-21. The figures originate from his stay in Rome, 1819-21; they are copies by H.E. Freund after statues by Bertel Thorvaldsen; they acquired pedestals of porphyry, which were thought to have been the Roman Emperors' favourite kind of stone in antiquity. Plateau, candelabras and centrepieces were purchased in 1822 in Paris from P. Thomire, who had been the chief purveyor to Napoleon I. Acquired by auction after Caroline Amalie, the Queen Mother, 1881.

2002. Table decoration of gilded bronze, made in Paris, possibly after drawings by G.F. Hetsch. Wedding present from Frederik VI to his daughter Caroline, 1829. Acquired by auction after the latter, 1881.

2003. Two mirrors, procured 1777 for the King's private secretary, Ove Høegh Guldberg, at Prinsens Palæ (now the National Museum). Designed by the architect C.F. Harsdorff and carved by J. Karleby.

2004.-2005. Christian VIII and Caroline Amalie, bronze busts by Bertel Thorvaldsen, 1821.

2006. Automaton clock with carillon and organ, theater and waterfalls. On the pedestal the coat-of-arms and device of Christian VII. Attributed to James Cox, London in c. 1780.

Room 21. The Long Hall. The Knights' Hall
The hall was originally intended as a dining-hall and ballroom. At the end of the 17th and beginning of the 18th centuries it was used for audiences and thereafter for festive occasions. The hall, the last to be furnished in the palace, was completed in 1624. The only original fixtures are the two Dutch fireplaces. As in Christian IV's other rooms, there were paintings in

the ceiling. Their motifs constituted a programme, and illustrated contemporary belief in the power of the planets over human destiny: a central band of square fields with obelisks, allegorical figures and Latin inscriptions (now in Rooms 10, 17 and 18). On each side were a number of large paintings, some of which are preserved at Kronborg today. In 1685, Christian V replaced the gilt leather wall-covering with tapestries, which in 1917 were transferred to the great hall at Christiansborg; however, two examples (nos. 2133 & 2134) are still hanging on either side of the thrones. At the beginning of the 18th century Frederik VI had German and Italian artists, among them Frederik Ehbisch and Carlo Maria Pozzi, put up the present stucco ceiling with the Danish coat-of-arms surrounded by the Orders of the Elephant and of the Dannebrog. The side reliefs depict historical events: the liberation of the serfs, the founding of the dragoons, the enlistment of the sailors, and the founding of the land militia. The cornice was marbled by Christian van Bracht. The ceiling paintings by Hendrick Krock display the regalia. Above the door of the Old Regalia Room is Christian V's portrait, a relief in marble, presumably by A.C. l'Amoureux; and above the exit is Frederik IV's portrait, a relief in plaster of Paris, signed: Dajon. Both are surrounded by wooden ornaments by Frederik Ehbisch. The hall contains one of the world's largest collections of silver furniture, mainly from the 18th century. Portraits of the kings and queens of Denmark from Christian IV to Christian VIII hang on the walls.

2101. Silver guéridons: Four tall guéridons made in Augsburg 1739-40 by Philipp Jacob (VI) Drentwett and Bernhard Heinrich Weye, after J.F. Blondel, 1735. Stood in Christian VI's Audience Chamber at Christiansborg. – To these belong the four ten-armed candelabra, altered in 1752 by Nicolai Langermann in Copenhagen. – Four guéridons, marked with the monogram of Princess Sophie Caroline of Ostfriesland, sister of Queen Sophie Magdalene, made in 1733 and

1736 by Ole Flores Wilcken in Copenhagen. Two guéridons, Augsburg work, made in 1708-10 by Johannes Bartermann. – Four guéridons with the crowned monogram of Princess Charlotte Amalie, made in Copenhagen, two by Carsten Hufnagel in 1732 and two by Ole Flores Wilcken in 1736. – Two guéridons made in Hamburg c. 1710 by Johan Adolph Sülssen.

2102. Frederik V as Crown Prince; full-length portrait painted by J.S. du Wahl, 1740 (pendant to no. 2152).

2103. Princess Magdalena Sibylla, wife of Christian, the Prince Elect, full-length. Painted by Karel van Mander c. 1635.

2104. Cabinet of walnut veneer, dyed sycamore and bone and in-laid with Florentine mosaic. Ebony foot. From c. 1660.

2105. Christian IV and Queen Anne Cathrine; Full-length. Origi-nally two separate portraits. The King painted by Pieter Isaacsz c. 1612?

2106. Table, the top of which bears a map of Denmark, inlaid in plaster of Paris stucco (scagliola), signed: I. Franciscus Bruno Napolitanus fecit. Made c. 1665.

2107. Two mirrors and six mirror sconces of silver, with the mono-gram of Frederik IV and parts of the Danish coat-of-arms, surrounded by rays. Made in Copenhagen 1706 by Hendrich Reinicke. Originally hung in the Marble Room (Room 5).

2108. Queen Sophie Amalie; oval, on copper, painted by Abra-ham Wuchters, c. 1680.

2109. Six armchairs and twelve high-backed chairs with monogram of Frederik IV; made in 1718 by Johan Weys; the covers were embroidered by Queen Charlotte Amalie and her la-dies. Two of the covers are signed: F.E. 1699 and 1700.

2110. Queen Charlotte Amalie. Oval, half-length, oil on copper. Painted by Jacob d'Agar?

2111. Ebony cabinet covered with tortoiseshell on red ground. Antwerp, c. 1660? Standing on the cabinet:
Tankard and covered cup of silver with inlaid Holstein coins with nettle leaves, lions on the covers, and feet in the form of the collared swans of Stormarn. Made for Hamburg's pro-jected acclamation of Frederik III in 1654. The cup is stamped with the mark of the goldsmith Jørgen Stilke (nos. 503, 5156-5160).

2112. Frederik III: oval, half-length, painted by Michael van Haven?

2113. Plaster of Paris bust of Frederik III, 1644? Probably by F. Dieussart. Saved from the Sophie Amalienborg fire.

2114. Christian IV. Marble bust from 1644. Made by F. Dieussart.

2115. Silver baptismal font, partly gilt. At the bottom there is a relief representing the baptism of Christ. Since 1671 used at the baptism of all the Royal princes and princesses. Hamburg work, made by Christian Mundt II, and foot by Gödert Botstede.

2116. Silver table with wooden top. Made by Andreas Normand. Used by the kings from 1795 until 1829 at the annual opening of the Supreme Court at Rosenborg. Belonging to this, a table cover of red velvet with Frederik IV's motto: Dominus mihi adjutor (The Lord my helper), in gold embroidery. (Used together with armchair no. 2118).

2117. The Royal Statute, printed 1709, in red velvet cover.

2118. Armchair of silver, made by the goldsmith Andreas Normand; with Frederik IV's monogram and the Norwegian Lion, in silver embroidery. Presented to the King by Queen Louise as a birthday present on 11th October 1715. (Used together with table no. 2116).

2119. Fountain for washing the hands, of ebony and silver, with figures depicting the myth of Diana and Acteon. In the drawers, toiletries. The fountain was made by Hans III Peters in Augsburg 1640-45, the toiletries by Daniel Zech. Belonged to Queen Sophie Amalie.

2120. Silver firescreen, with relief depicting Mars, Venus and Cupid. Augsburg work from 1732-33 by P.J. (VI) Drentwett. Centre relief by J.A. Thelott.

2121. Armchair with chased silver covering; made by A.F. Holling in Copenhagen, 1740, for Christian VI's Audience Chamber at Christiansborg Palace.

2122. Christian V and Queen Charlotte Amalie, two three-quarter length portraits, painted by Jacob d'Agar.

2123. Ebony cupboard with coloured inlays of sycamore and bone. Inside ivory veneered triumphal arch, dated 1697, and mirror vestibule. Made by cabinetmaker Lorenz Corbianus to commemorate the Scanian War.

Standing on the cupboard:

Silver tankard, made 1584 for Duke Julius of Brunswick-Lüneburg (1528-89).

Also »Welcome to Hørsholm« fountain of silver gilt with container in the shape of a pineapple. Jeremias Sibenbürger, Augsburg c. 1650.

Large covered cup of silver, richly engraved with i.a. illustration of tilting at the ring; belonged to Queen Sophie Amalie's brother, Duke Christian Ludvig of Brunswick-Lüneburg (1622-65). Made by Evert Kettwych, Hamburg c. 1641.

2124. Queen Louise. Full-length, presumably painted by J.S. du Wahl.

2125. Frederik IV. Full-length by H. Krock; the face was painted by N. Wichmann.

2126. Christian V as a child, with his toy cannons (see no. 2127). Attributed to K. van Mander, c. 1650.

2127. Christian V's toy cannons.

2128. Two mirrors in silver frames with matching console tables of silver, made from designs by Court Sculptor Louis-Augustin le Clerc? The mirrors are Augsburg work by Philipp Jacob (VI) Drentwett and Bernhard Heinrich Weye 1739-40. One of the console tables by P.J. (VI) Drentwett 1739, the other by Ole Flores Wilcken in Copenhagen 1740. From Christian VI's Audience Chamber at Christiansborg, where they were saved from the fire in 1794. Mirror glass renewed. (See also nos. 2101 and 2121).

2129. Two Chinese porcelain vases, from the K'ang-hsi period with mounting of gilt silver bearing the monogram of Queen Louise. By G. Bolch in Copenhagen, 1704.

2130. Queen Sophie Magdalene, painted by J.S. du Wahl.

2131. Christian VI, painted by J.S. du Wahl.

2132. Queen Sophie Magdalene, painted by Andreas Møller.
Two of the twelve tapestries, hung in the hall in the time of Christian V:

2133. The capture of Helsingborg, 3rd July 1676. Christian V can be seen in the foreground (with red coat); on his right, Prince Jørgen. Executed by Bernt van der Eichen.

2134. The landing at Råå, 29th June 1676. In the foreground, the transport fleet, and close to the coast of Scania, the escorting warships.

2135. Cabinet covered with richly ornamented and chased silver plates, c. 1680. Made in Copenhagen by Jean Henri de Moor? Carved, gilt stand, c. 1740.
Standing on the cabinet:
Silver cup from a tilting joust in Oldenborg 1635, won by Prince Frederik (III).
Silver tankard of chased silver with mythological motifs, by Hermann Lambrecht of Hamburg, c. 1650.
Mug of lignum vitæ, silver-mounted and signed: L.B. 1672, made by Lars Berthelsen, parish clerk of the Church of the Holy Ghost in Copenhagen.

2136. Three lions of chased silver, made 1665-1670 in Copenhagen by Ferdinand Küblich. Used on solemn occasions right up to the present time as guards around the throne and the Royal catafalque.

2137. The coronation chair of the Danish kings, made of narwhal tusks by Bendix Grodtschiliing 1662-1671: the gilt figures were made by J. Kohlmann and added in Christian V's time. Used at coronations from 1671-1840.

2138. The silver coronation chair of the Danish queens; made for Queen Sophie Magdalene by Niels Jonsen of Copenhagen in 1731.

2139. Two candlesticks of gilt silver, made in Copenhagen 1732 by Ole Flores Wilcken.
2140. Table, with foot of carved, gilded wood with Frederik III's monogram from c. 1650. The top is of imitation marble with indistinct signature: BN, possibly for Franciscus Bruno Napolitanus (no. 2106).
2141. Silver cup representing the celestial globe, crowned by Zeus and borne by Neptune. Hinrich Lambrecht II, Hamburg c. 1650.
2142. Two large silver cups with the celestial sphere and the earthly globe, supported, respectively, by Atlas and a Triton and with Mars and Juno on the top. Hamburg work c. 1650 by Peter Ohr (I).
2144. Christian VII in his coronation robes. Full-length, painted by Jens Juel, 1789.
2145. Queen Caroline Amalie, painted by J.D. Court 1841.
2146. Christian VIII, painted by J.D. Court 1841.
2148. Table covered with chased silver plates. The foot made by Johann I Bartermann, the top by Johann Heinrich Mannlich, Augsburg, 1708-10.
2150. Frederik VI, painted by F.C. Grøger, c. 1808.
2151. Queen Marie, painted by F.C. Grøger, 1808.
2152. Christian VI, full-length portrait painted by J.S. du Wahl. Gift from the King to General Grüner, who was Ambassador in Stockholm, 1740-43.
2153. Folding screen made of rye and wheat straw, decorated with rural scenes, c. 1675.

Room 22. The Glass Cabinet

The fireplace is from Christian IV's time, but was given Frederik III's monogram presumably at the same time as his wife had the elevator installed (p. 8). During the time of Christian V, this was the Picture Cabinet, containing small intimate paintings, the so-called cabinet pieces.

In 1709 Frederik IV visited Venice, which had for centuries been Europe's chief producer of glass. He was presented with an exquisite collection of glass by the Venetian Senate. With this in mind, the King had this room furnished 1713-14. It was modelled on the Porcelain Cabinet at Charlottenburg in Berlin, which Frederik IV visited on his journey home. Porcelain cabinets of this type were in fashion in Europe at the end of the 17th century, but this is the only known glass cabinet. The architect was Chief Fire Officer Gottfried Fuchs: for the glass, he built consoles in pyramid form, covered with marbled paper and edged with festoons of lead gilt. The walls were covered with silk, and on the ceiling was a painting of Bacchus, the god of wine, by Lorenz and Marcus Cardes.

Of the originally close on 1000 glass pieces, only about 750 are preserved. They can be divided into four groups:

The Venetian group includes clear glass with vari-coloured flowers, parrots, blue threads and gilt masks; glass with inlaid white threads in counter-running concentric circles, *a reticello*, or twisted in ribs, *a retorti*; blue glass with white wavy lines, *a penne*; and milky blue opal glass, and yellow and red glass.

The second group consists of clear, thin-walled glass with shields, festoons, leaf and ribband work in mat engraving. These were made in Saxony, 1700-1714.

The third group consists of dark red Ruby glass melted with gold. They have Augsburg mountings of gilded silver and were probably made in South Germany around 1700.

The fourth group is mainly glass inherited by Frederik IV, for example, Frederik II's six-pint humpen from 1568. It also includes glass from the Netherlands, Nüremburg, Bohemia, Silesia, Potsdam, Cassel and England, as well as some that were probably made for Christian V in the glass works at Christianshavn 1688-92.

The teeming mass of glass is matched by the crowded walls: there are Venetian miniatures in ivory f. ex. by Rosalba Carriera (under the window), reliefs by Gottfried Wolffram and Magnus Berg, and paintings by artists including Karel van Mander and Wolfgang Heimbach.

Room 23. The Porcelain Cabinet

Frederik IV had originally planned to have a porcelain cabinet to correspond with the glass cabinet, but for unknown reasons it was never realized. The present interior is from c. 1860 and contains a number of sets of old porcelain belonging to the Royal House.

2301. Part of a set of Meissen porcelain. Made for Christian VI, probably around 1740-45.
2302. Portrait of Frederik V, painted by Töpfer, 1752, on a pedestal. Meissen porcelain.
2303. Pieces of Böttger's brown Saxon stoneware, forerunner of the Meissen porcelain. Dresden, c. 1715.
2304. Tureen of Meissen porcelain with the coat-of-arms of Count J.H.E. Bernstoff, c. 1740.
2305. Flora Danica porcelain. Made 1790-1803 at the Royal Copenhagen Porcelain Manufactory, decorated with botanical drawings of Denmark's flora. Tradition has it that it was commisioned as a gift for Catharine the Great of Russia, who died, however, before the set was finished. It is still used by the Royal Family on special occasions.
2306. Vase with the goddess of fame, and Apollon and Minerva *en grisaille*. Made at the Royal Copenhagen Porcelain Manufactory in 1789 and bought by Crown Prince Frederik VI as a birthday present to himself 1790. The form is repeated in the two vases on each side of the plinth. Saved from the fire at Christiansborg 1794.
2307. Two vases: egg-shaped with goats' heads and cupids. Modelled 1789, possibly by C.A. Luplau. The so-called mermaid vase *en grisaille* after J.F. Saly. Delivered to Crown Prince Frederik VI on New Year's Eve 1788. Royal Copenhagen Porcelain. Saved from the fire at Christiansborg 1794.
2308. Three covered vases of Royal Copenhagen Porcelain with portraits of Frederik VI as Crown Prince, Juliane Marie, the Queen Mother, and Princess Louise Augusta. 1780's.
2309. Flower painting on Royal Copenhagen Porcelain, executed by J.L. Jensen, c. 1830.
2310. Two plates of Royal Copenhagen Porcelain, dated 4th September 1780 (Juliane Marie, the Queen Mother's birthday).
2311. Swedish faience, made at Marieberg in 1774.
2312. Breakfast service of Royal Copenhagen Porcelain bearing a crowned F in flowers, delivered to Crown Prince Frederik VI 1785.
2313. Table with top of Schleswig faience.
2314. Punchbowl of Royal Copenhagen Porcelain, portraying the

Battle of the Roads of Copenhagen on 2nd April, 1801. Presented by Count Roepstorff to one of the non-commissioned officers who took part in the battle.

2316. The Juliane Marie Service; Chinese porcelain portraying the equestrian statue of Frederik V at Amalienborg, after a drawing by Peter Cramer.

2317. Punchbowl of Chinese porcelain, portraying Peter Appleby's rope-walk and shipyard at Christianshavn.

2318. Punchbowl of Chinese porcelain decorated in iron-red and portraying Our Saviour's Church in Copenhagen.

2319. Two plates of Chinese export porcelain with the inscription: For the happy sons of the right of citizenship.

2320. Various porcelain pieces of Chinese origin. The two big »famille rose« jars and the two big, round basins belonged to Sophie Magdalene at Hirschholm Palace.

2321.-2322. Table service of Japanese porcelain with octagonal dishes. Belonging to this is the centrepiece with the coats-of-arms of Christian VI and Queen Sophie Magdalene.

2323. Two plates of Chinese export porcelain portraying the Reformed Church in Copenhagen, 1750.

2324. Sèvres porcelain presented to Christian VII in 1768 when he visited the factory.

Three paintings on Sèvres porcelain:

2325. Cupid, after a painting by Charles van Loo.

2326. A Love Sacrifice, after Pierre.

2327. A Camp Scene.

Room 24. The Old Regalia Room
(temporarily closed to the public)

During the Absolutist period, this tower room was the Treasury. Christian V kept the regalia here, as well as the major part of the royal treasures in the form of gold and precious stones, which were housed in two wallcupboards, still in existence. In the adjacent »Green Cabinet« (a small velvet-lined room in the tower extension behind the panel door on the right) were displayed the »next best« possessions: »curiosities«, miniature portraits, cameos and parade arms. When Rosenborg was converted into a museum in the 19th century, the contents of the two cabinets were distributed in the rooms representing the various *64* kings. The regalia, however, were put on display for the first time in Christian V's Room in 1922. With the opening of the underground Treasury in 1975 and the Green Cabinet in the basement in 1994, regalia and applied arts are once again assembled.

Nothing remains of the original tower room decorations; the stucco ceiling, made by C.L. Fossati, dates from a restoration in 1762.

The Basement with the Green Cabinet and the Treasury

A door in the middle of the stair turret's facade leads to the palace basement. The whitewashed cellar vaults have remained almost unchanged since the time of Christian IV. In the foremost room stand the limestone statues that once adorned the gatehouse gables. Badly weathered, the figures were replaced around 1866 with zinc replicas, which in turn were replaced in the 1930s by the present limestone copies. Behind one of the two iron doors bearing the date 1681 is the royal wine cellar, which is still in use. Here, too, is the cask of »Rosenborg Wine« laid down by Christian IV. The other barrels are dated 1597 and 1599. Behind the other iron door is a vault (under the Great Tower) where Christian V kept a fortune in gold coins, possibly in the four iron chests.

A room to the left leads to a barrel-vaulted room, the cellar of the first Rosenborg, which was recreated in a restoration in 1993. In the foremost half of the room are exhibited riding trappings and parade arms, the earliest of which originate from Christian IV's collections at Sparepenge in the gardens of Frederiksborg. At Rosenborg the saddles were housed in a wallcupboard in the Old Regalia Room, while the weapons were hung on the walls of the Green Cabinet together with the best arms and walking sticks of Frederik III and Christian V.

3000. Christian IV's riding trappings, used at his coronation in 1596. Black velvet embroidered with gold and pearls. Made by Peter Paul Perlestikker in Copenhagen.

3002.-3004. Stirrups and spurs (belonging to no. 3000). Iron and gold with enamel and diamonds. Made by Dirich Fyring, who made Christian IV's crown?

3006. Sword-hanger. Leather and silk with gold, silver and pearl embroidery of the Pelican in her Piety; the symbol of the Martyrdom of Christ. Used at the coronation in 1596 (no. 5124)?

3008. Helmet of velvet with gold embroidery. Worn by Christian IV on his way to Copenhagen Cathedral to be crowned in 1596?

3010. Riding trappings used at the wedding of Christian, the Prince Elect in 1634. Black velvet, embroidered with gold, jewels and pearls. Made by Gert Osserijn in Copenhagen, partly by re-using older pieces of jewellery.

3012.-3014. Spurs (belonging to no.3010) of gold with diamonds.

3016.-3018. A pair of pistols. Pommels and mounts of gold with enamel, sapphires and diamonds. Made by Dirich Fyring for Christian IV's coronation in 1596, but used again in 1634? Pommels and mounts were originally part of ivory pistols. Around 1830 they were transferred to the present pistols from 1690, signed: Heinrich Kappel Kopenhagen.

3654. Christian IV's Admiral's Sword from 1617 with velvet scabbard containing nautical and artillerist measuring instruments. Signed: Christoph Trechsler der Elter Mechanicus Dresden.

3655. Sword with gilt and enamelled hilt, Christian IV's monogram and the three Danish lions. Worn by the King as a side arm at his coronation in 1596. Made by Mogens Winter in Copenhagen.

3656. Christian IV's accolade rapier from c. 1617. Hilt with foliage in gold on blue *champlevé* enamel, set with pointed and table-cut diamonds. The blade is signed: De Tomas / De Aiala.

3657. Rapier worn by the Prince Elect c. 1620. Hilt with blue and white gold enamel richly set with table-cut diamonds.

3658.-3660. Rapier, scabbard and spurs. The sword hilt is formed of three snakes, each biting a heart. Gold, enamel and diamonds. Scabbard of brown leather with snake-head motif. Rowel spurs of iron with heavy gold plating and enamelled snakes and hearts. The snakes symbolize wisdom and the hearts courage. Belonged to the Prince Elect. Made for his wedding in 1634? (no. 3010)

3661.-3662. Rapier with belt. The rapier's gold enamel hilt has a pommel in the form of an animal's head, and quillons in the form of a dragon. The blade is signed: Peter Munich. The belt is mounted with snake and mollusc motifs. Belonged to the Prince Elect. Made for his wedding in 1634? (no. 3010)

3663. Traditionally thought to be Frederik III's »Command Rapier« from the Torstenson War of 1644, with which he severed the arm of a Swede. Blade made by Clemens Dinger, Solingen.

3664. Deer-hunting sword with knife, sheath and belt, decorated with horn, gold and flower enamel. Belonged to Queen Sophie Amalie.

3665.-3666. A pair of rowel spurs with enamelled lions.

3667. Dress Rapier with hilt of gilded copper, c. 1650. Belonged to Frederik III.

3668.-3670. Rapier and spurs mounted with alchemist gold; possibly made by Frederik III's physician Peter Bülche.

3671. Christian V's baton with crown set with diamonds.

3672. Dress Rapier with silver hilt, worn by Christian V as Crown Prince. On the blade: De Alonso Perez en Toledo.

3673. Rapier with agate and garnets, used by Christian V in carrousel riding at Gottorp in 1686.

3674. Hunting set with sword, hunting knife, various smaller knives and belts. Hilts of agate inlaid in silver gilt. France, c. 1680?

3675. Hunting knife with two smaller knives in a sheath. Belonged with the foregoing.

3676. Rapier of steel. Traditionally thought to have been used by Christian V in the Scanian War; the blade is German or Italian.

3677. Christian V's whip with diamonds.

Oriental weapons from Persia and the Ottoman Empire were highly prized royal gifts in the 17th century. Of the present exhibits, the two daggers were possibly part of a gift from Czar Michail Romanov to Christian IV in 1622:

3678. Dagger of gold with hilt of agate and sheath of goatskin, set with rubies and turquoises.

3679. Dagger and sheath of gold, set with rubies, rose quartz, turquoises and pearls.

3680. Right vambrace of gold, set with turquoises and rubies, lining of silk, straps of leather.

3681.-3683. Three fencing and close combat shields, mounted with gold and set with turquoises and rubies; two with lining of Persian silk velvet.

3685. Head decoration for a horse. Silver gilt with jade, turquoises and rubies.

3686. Walking stick of ebony and ivory. Bust of Queen Charlotte Amalie carved by Gottfried Wolffram, c. 1690?

3686. Walking stick with sundial and red lacquer. Belonged to Christian V.

3690. Walking stick of cane and silver with artillerist measuring instruments and Dutch measures. Belonged to Christian V as Crown Prince. The Netherlands, the 1660s.

3691. Similar calibre gauge with gold knob and Danish measurements.

3692. Walking stick of bamboo. Knob of enamelled gold with the motto: Chacun a son Tour. Commissioned by Frederik III in commemoration of the Swedish King Carl X Gustav's sudden death in 1660, the year after his army had stormed Copenhagen. Made by Paul Kurtz?

3693. Calibre gauge with battle hammer of alchemist gold, possibly made by Frederik III's physician Peter Bülche.

3694. Walking stick of narwhal tusk (unicorn horn). The rubies on the knob conceal holes to a cavity containing aromatic ointment. Enamelling by Paul Kurtz (no. 4023) in 1663?

A door to the left leads to
Ole Rømer's Room

Ole Rømer was born in 1644 in Århus, and died in 1710 in Copenhagen. After completing his studies in astronomy at the University of Copenhagen, he lived and worked from 1672-81 at the Paris Observatory. In the course of his observations of Jupiter's satellites he discovered the »procrastination«, or speed, of light, bringing him international fame. In 1680 he demonstrated a planet machine, (a planetarium), and a machine for calculating the Moon's eclipses, (an eclipsarium), to the Académie des Sciences in Paris and to King Louis XIV. Both machines are still preserved in Paris. Christian V acquired a corresponding set in 1682. In 1685 similar sets were presented to the King of Siam and the Emperor of China. It is not known whether these have been preserved.

On his return to Denmark in 1681, Ole Rømer became the King's trusted adviser in all technical matters. He rationalised a number of existing systems and introduced a uniform system of weights and measures. The original »national standard prototypes«, presented to the King in 1683/84, can be seen in this room.

3700. Planetarium. Constructed by Ole Rømer to demonstrate the orbit of the planets round the Sun. Made in Paris 1678-79 by Isaac Thuret, royal clockmaker.

3702. Eclipsarium. Constructed by Ole Rømer to calculate the Moon's orbit and eclipses. Made in Paris 1678-79 by Isaac Thuret, royal clockmaker.

3704. Cubic foot of bronze and iron. 1683. Inside measurement of eacg section 31.5 cm (= 1 Rhenish foot).

3706. A quart (approx.) measure of bronze. 1683. Holds 979 gr. water.

3708. A quart (approx.) measure of pewter.

3710. A pint (approx.) of pewter. 1683.

3712. A »yardstick« (63 cm = approx. 2 ft.) of ebony and silver. 1683.

3714. Weights of bronze. Dated 1684. 1 *lispund* equals 16 lbs. After 1686/87, 1 lb equalled 499.7 gr. The biggest weight weighs 10 *lispund*, equal to 80 kg.

3716. Weights of bronze in boxes of inlaid wood. 1683. The small weights have been missing for many years.

3718. Scales of brass and iron. 1683.

»Curiosities«, jewelry, cameos and miniature portraits from the Green Cabinet are displayed in the rear half of the basement. This collection was founded by Frederik III, as can be confirmed by the commission of Rosenborg's castellan dated 1663 and by paintings showing some of the items (nos. 4027 and 4072) signed by Cornelis Gijsbrecht 1670. Travel accounts indicate that in the early 1670s these items were exhibited in rooms on the first floor of the palace, but when Christian V had the Long Hall modernized and the regalia moved to Rosenborg, the Green Cabinet was furnished on the same occasion. The collection was housed in a large wallcupboard with double-leaf doors, the standing items distributed on four shelves and the bottom, the hanging items on the back wall between the shelves attached to pieces of board which were covered with velvet and edged with gold galloons, called »papper«. The items were categorized as to both material and function, and the whole arranged in accordance with decorative symmetrical principles, with the largest and and most impressive item in the centre. As Rosenborg's oldest furnishings from 1696 are only partly preserved, the complete contents of the Green Cabinet are only known from the inventory of 1718. In the meantime, some items had gone and others had been included, but the principles for their display remained unchanged. These have been retained in the present reconstruction, so that for each of the four shelves and the bottom there is a corresponding glass case, while the items that were on the back wall between the shelves are seen in a wall case.

The items cover a time span from c. 1450 to 1718. By and large, they represent what remained of the royal legacy after the Reformation in 1536 and following the defeats in the 30 Years' War and the wars with Sweden. Many of the items were royal gifts originating from the personal collections of royal personages such as, for example, Leonora Christina and Corfitz Ulfeldt, Frederik III's and Christian V's wives: Queen Sophie Amalie and Queen Charlotte Amalie. Another addition was the Duke of Holstein-Gottorp's collection which was transferred to Rosenborg after the fall of Gottorp during the Great Northern War in 1713.

From the back wall above the top shelf (everything of ivory unless otherwise stated).

4001. The Adoration of the Shepherds. Relief after a drawing by Johannes Rottenhammer. Gottfried Wolffram?

4002. Christian V on horseback in front of Copenhagen. Medallion. Gottfried Wolffram, 1693?

4003. The Battle of Køge Bugt 1677. Medallion commemorating the Danish victory over the Swedish navy in the Scanian War. After Christopher Schneider's gold medal from c. 1685. Gottfried Wolffram?

4004. Apollo flaying Marsyas. The relief depicts the punishment of the gods. After a painting by Jan Liss. Joachim Henne, c. 1680?

4005. Venus with Amor, Ceres and Bacchus. The relief illustrates luxurious living, since there can be no love without bread and wine. After an original by Rubens.

4006. The Golden Age. Relief. Joachim Henne?

4007. Venus and Adonis. The hunt calls, but Venus tries to hold Adonis back. The relief illustrates desire and duty. Joachim Henne?

4009. Christian V and Queen Charlotte Amalie. Double medallion. Wilhelm Heinrich Wessel 1684.

4010. Charlotte Amalie as Ceres. Medallion. Joachim Henne, c. 1670?

4011. Charlotte Amalie. Medallion, signed: GW for Gottfried Wolffram, c. 1690.

4013.-4014. Powder horns. Northern India (Mughal), 17th cent.

4016.-4017. Two small recorders of narwhal tusk. One made by a professional instrument-maker, the other by an amateur. From c. 1650?

4018.-4019. Knife handle and paper folder.

4020. A bobbin mounted in gold with enamelled forget-me-nots. Believed to have been turned by Christian IV as a gift to Queen Anne Cathrine c. 1600?

From the top shelf;

4022. Tankard of ivory with carving of the drunken Silenus. Mounting of silver gilt, stamped for Andreas I Wickert, Augsburg 1640-45.

4023. Cup of narwhal tusk, gold and enamel. On the lid a Greenlander symbolizing the Danish king's mastery of the northern seas. Carved by Jacob Jensen Nordmand 1662; mounting attributed to Paul Kurtz, 1663?

4025. Tankard of pierced ivory with amorous scenes, incl. Susanna bathing, and Lot and his daughters. Mounting of silver gilt, stamped for Heinrich (IV) Hintze, Lübeck c. 1650.

4027. Tankard of ivory with carving of the Rape of the Sabine Women. Mounting of silver gilt; inside the lid Frederik III's monogram. Carved by Joachim Henne 1667-70.

4029. Tankard of ivory with carving of battle scenes. On the lid a medaillion of Christian V on horseback crowned with laurels. Denmark, c. 1680?

4030. Tankard of narwhal tusk, mounted in silver gilt. On the lid a medallion of Hiob and Gunelle, two of the four Greenlanders who came to Denmark in 1654. Carved by Jacob Jensen Nordmand?

4031. Tankard of walrus tusk, mounted in silver. Carved by Jacob Jensen Nordmand?

4032. Covered beaker of ivory and silver gilt. The relief is based on a painting by Jan Liss of soldiers and harlots carousing, symbolizing the vices. Gottfried Wolffram, c. 1690?

4035. Beaker of ivory with carving of the myth of Diana and Actaeon.

4040. Goblet of ivory with carving of the Judgement of Paris, mounted in silver gilt. Joachim Henne, 1670- 80?

4042. Tankard of narwhal tusk, mother-of-pearl and silver gilt. On the lid engraved Paschal Lamb, inside Christ and the Woman of Samaria. Jacob Jensen Nordmand, 1651.

4044.-4045. Bagpipe player and spinning woman. Statuettes of ivory and glass. Illustrations of characters the aristocracy might choose for informal fancy dress balls, the so-called »Wirtschaften«. The Netherlands or Dresden, c. 1650.

4048.-4051. Four putti of ivory symbolizing the four seasons of spring, summer, autumn (winter replaced by air).

4056.-4058. Three putti of ivory with symbols of fire, water and air. Joachim Henne?

4063. Man answering the call of nature. Snuffbox of ivory with the crown of a hat as screwtop.

4046. Shepherd's pipe with amorous couple. Ivory.

4065.-4066. Two boxes of ivory with carved landscapes; on the lids the lacquered monograms of Christian V and Queen Charlotte Amalie. Gottfried Wolffram, 1699.

4068. Pen case of ivory. Andoin Schæff, 1680s?

4072. Hercules struggling with the vices. Statuette of box-wood. Joachim Henne, 1670.

From the 2nd shelf from the top and the wall behind it:

4073.-4074. Two spoons with mother-of-pearl bowls and stems of jet, c. 1600.

4077.-4080. Four spoons of rock crystal with serpentine silver gilt stems. Made for the Prince Elect, whose favourite motif was the serpent. (nos. 3658-3660)?

4081. Amulet of rock crystal and silver for jequirity, limestone from the stomach of the crayfish, which was a treasured antidote for eye disorders, heartburn, bladder stones, headaches, flatulence and syphilis. Rock crystal was also effective i.a. against thirst and toothache.

4082. The Tuscany Brilliant; a copy of a large brilliant, part of the Florentine crown jewels. Made of rock crystal with silver gilt mounting; brought back from Italy by Frederik IV in 1709?

4084. Dish of rock crystal mounted in gold with flower enamel. South Germany, c. 1640.

4086. Globe-shaped covered cup of rock crystal. Presumably 12th-13th century Romanesque work from the Rhine-Mosel district, mounted in silver gilt c. 1650.

4087. Goblet of rock crystal mounted in gold with enamel and diamonds. The goblet was originally covered, and was carved Freiburg im Breisgau 1550-1600. The mounting was added in stages between 1650 and 1718.

4089. Standing cup of rock crystal in the shape of a flying fish, presented to Christian V by Queen Sophie Amalie after the fall of Wismar in 1675. Made at the Saracchi studio in Milan c. 1580.

4091. Covered cup of rock crystal showing Hercules' fight with the Nemean Lion and the Hydra. The cup consists of separate pieces, assembled and mounted in the 17th century. The high-domed cover, the cylinder and foot were made at the Saracchi studio in Milan at the end of the 16th century.

4092. Goblet of rock crystal supported by a winged genius. On the foot the arms and motto of the Landgrave Carl of Hesse. Signed C.Labert fecit Cassel 1689. Presented to Christian V, brother-in-law of the Landgrave.

4096. Jewel box of cut-glass panes with silver gilt mounting and flower enamel feet. Cutting by Paul Schindler c. 1650-60.

4097.-4098. A pair of covered jars, engraved with figures and the months of the year. Nuremberg, 1640s?

4102. Bowl of smoky topaz in the form of a mussel with a lion's mask. The Miseroni studio in Milan 1600-1610.

4103. Vase of smoky topaz with diamond cutting. Carved by Ottavio Miseroni in Prague c. 1620.

4105. Monstrance clock of brass gilt and rock crystal. Minute and hour hands, date and phases of the moon, striking on the hour and each quarter. Signed: ZLA. Southern Germany, c. 1610.

4106.-4107. Christian V on horseback; miniature statuettes on marbled columns, made by Johan or Carl Christian van Bracht, c. 1690.

4108. Bowl of Islandic rock crystal, carved by Denis Piengart 1696?

4111. Dressing case of rock crystal, gold and enamel with toilet requisites, c. 1620?

4412. Neck watch. Dial of gold with diamonds and enamel (*en resille sur verre*). Octagonal case of facetted rock crystal. Clockwork signed by Caspar Cameel, Strasbourg c. 1620; case made in Freiburg im Breisgau.

4113. Table bell of rock crystal, wound with gold thread. South Germany, c. 1600. Belonged to Leonora Christina.

4114.-4115. Two glass flagons, engraved with Queen Sophie Amalie's monogram and arms. Nuremberg, c. 1660?

4118.-4119. Two signets of rock crystal with lions. China, 17th cent.

4122.-4123. Two table decorations of Islandic rock crystal with Norwegian amethysts. Made by Denis Piengart c. 1690 to illustrate the occurrence of minerals in the King's northern provinces?

4124. Standing cup of coconut mounted in silver gilt. Carving shows the creation of Eve, the Fall and the Expulsion from the Garden of Eden. Nuremberg, c. 1550.

4125.-4126. Two covered beakers of gold ruby glass, blown in Schlackenwerth or Reichstadt in Bohemia, and polished by Duke Julius Franz of Saxony-Lauenburg before 1689; the earliest dated examples of the gold ruby glass to which alchemists of the Baroque attributed magical and healing powers.

4133. Covered goblet of rock crystal, engraved with dallying hens and chickens, illustrating the proverb: Aus diesem Spiel, sind worden viel.

4134. Knife. In silver on the stem FS, Frederik II's monogram, the year 1570 and MHZGA, the royal motto: Mein Hoffnung Zu Gott Allein.

4135. Beaker engraved with scenes from the Swedish Wars 1658-60: Frederik III on horseback in front of Copenhagen, the sortie on Amager, the battle of Nyborg and the sea battle of The Sound. Signed: JVS? Nuremberg or Saxony, 1660s?

From the back wall above the 3rd shelf:

4140. Pendant in the form of a dolphin with toothpick and earpick. Pearl mounted in enamelled gold with diamonds and rubies. Germany, 1570-90. Large natural pearls were in fashion and hygiene was a sign of rank.

4141. Carrousel riding prize with portrait of Princess Ulrika Eleonora, contest scene and inscription: To the most agile, won by Christian V 1678. Gold with enamel and diamonds; enamel ascribed to Paul Prieur.

4142. Relief medallion of Diana, composed of semi-precious stones of different colours. Ottavio Miseroni in Prague, c. 1605.

4143. Emperor Rudolf II, cameo of shell, mounted in a frame of 24 rubies and crown of gold enamel. Cameo South Germany, c. 1600; mounting c. 1650.

4146. Ring of enamelled gold with 22 diamonds, upon which a woman's hand grasping a phallos; inside inscription: TAM-QVAM NON HABENS. Possibly Frederik III's comment on Queen Sophie Amalie's affair with the valet Jacob Petersen which was discovered in 1664, when the King and Queen had been married for 22 years.

4147. Cupid. Pendant of enamelled gold with rubies and diamonds. The Nederlands, c. 1600. A similar item of jewellery was part of Queen Anne Cathrine's dowry in 1597.

4150. Carrousel riding prize, donated by Queen Charlotte Amalie. Belongs together with no. 4141.

4151. Bust of an emperor. Chalcedony cameo in gold mount. Italy, 1550-1600?

4154. Crane. Pendant of pearls and enamelled gold with diamonds, rubies and emeralds. The crane is holding a stone in each claw, symbolizing vigilance, since if it fell asleep it would drop the stones and wake up. Northern Europe, c. 1610.

4155. Monkey's head. Pomander of girasol in enamelled gold. Inside an aromatic sponge and enamelled motifs with French inscriptions satirizing human frailty. On the back a mirror. Belonged to Leonora Christina; purchased at Corfitz Ulfeldt's embassy in Paris 1647?

4157. Carrousel riding prize donated by the Dowager Queen Sophie Amalie. Belongs with nos. 4141 and 4150.

4158. Omphale. Cameo of onyx mounted in silver gilt. A favourite motif in Greek legend was Hercules' sojourn with Omphale, Queen of Lydia, where he dressed as a woman and spun wool with her terns while Omphale wore his lionskin. Italy, 1550-1600.

4161. Lucretia. Pendant of chalcedony, mounted in gold with rubies and emeralds. France, c. 1550.

4179. Hercules. Onyx cameo mounted in gold. Italy 1550-1600?

4188. The Virgin Mary? Medallion of so-called aventurine glass with »grains of gold« of crystallized copper oxide. Made in Venice by Vicenzo Miotti? Brought back by Frederik IV from Italy in 1709?

4196. The Adoration of the Magi. Cameo of onyx mounted in gold with enamel. Alessandro Masnago or studio in Milan 1575-1600?

4204. Locket with cameo of Hercules and the Nemian Lion, surrounded by the heads of 13 emperors. Hercules carved after a drawing by Albrecht Dürer from 1511 and belonging to a group of shell cameos from c. 1520, made in Nuremberg or France. The emperor series, of onyx, is later. The enamelled mounting with green stones can be dated to c. 1630.

4213. Female figure in enamel. Burgundian work from c. 1500?

4219. Emperor Ferdinand I. Shell cameo mounted in silver. Part of an emperor series.

4223. Horse and man. Sardonyx cameo in silver gilt mounting. Alessandro Masnago or studio, Milan 1575-1600?

4229. Young Roman. Sardonyx cameo.

4233. Hat medallion showing Mars. Onyx, ivory, lapis lazuli and enamelled gold. France, c. 1550.

4242. Christian, the Prince Elect. Cameo of bloodstone mounted in gold enamel. Below the shoulder PEC: Pietas Et Constantia, the Prince's motto. Denmark, 1620-30.

4246. Julius Caesar. Cameo of onyx in gold mounting. 17th cent.

4250. The Landing of Noah's Ark. Onyx cameo after an engraving by Bernhard Salomon 1554. Ascribed to Alessandro Masnago or studio in Milan 1575-1600. Mounted as a pendant in enamelled gold. On the back a crowned K for Kirsten Munk, Christian IV's morganatic wife. Confiscated from her daughter, Leonora Christina, by Frederik III.

4258. St Paul. Cameo of zircon, mounted in a pomander of gold enamel with rubies and pendant pearls. On the back, lid of a capsule to contain spices. On the cameo the name of St Paul and the year 41. Northern Europe, 1641?

4278.-4280. Knife, fork and spoon with handles of agate in enamelled gold. Johann Kobenhaupt or studio, Stuttgart, 1609-1623.

4282.-4285. Knife and fork with handles of agate mounted in silver; the blade with stamped mark for William Balls, London Cutlers' Company, 1630-50.

4291. Knive with hilt of agate mounted in silver; the blade stamped with mark for the London Cutlers' Company, 1606-25.

4297.-4298. Knife and fork mounted in gold enamel with garnets; blade with stamped harpoon. 1575-1600?

From the 3rd shelf from the top:

4310. Standing cup and cover of heliotrope, mounted in enamelled gold and set with cameos. France, c. 1650?

4313. Standing cup of agate, mounted in enamelled gold. As cover finial Venus with a dolphin. Johann Kobenhaupt or studio, Stuttgart, 1609-23.

4316. Standing cup and cover of agate, mounted in gold enamel with rubies. Paris, 1620-50.

4317. Goblet of garnet, mounted in gold with flower enamel and pearls. The body dates possibly from antiquity and was presumably a separate bowl. Carved by Dionysio Miseroni and mounted by Hanns Reinhardt Taravell in Prague in 1655.

4318. Salt of agate, mounted in enamelled and gilt silver. Possibly turned in Venice in the 15th cent. or as »New Gothic« in the early 17th cent.; mounted in Germany, 1600-1630.

4319.-4320. Two standing cups of agate, mounted in gold enamel. Paris 1630-50?

4333. Mussel-shaped standing cup and cover of bloodstone, carved at the Miseroni studio in Milan or Prague. Gold enamel mounting by Jan Vermeyen, maker of Emperor Rudolph II's cown, in Prague c. 1600.

4335. Octofoil bowl of honey-coloured agate, the wall carved with arching separated by fluting. The shape is reminiscent of Mughal hardstone carving; the gravity suggests Europe, 17th century.

4336. Bowl of chalcedony onyx. The tapering oval shape and parrot handles are known both in Ottoman and Mughal metalwork. Turkey or India, 17th century.

4337.-4338. Presentation tray and covered cup of agate, mounted in enamelled gold. Augsburg, 1650?

4353.-4354. Two salts of agate; mounted by Jan Vermeyen or studio, Prague 1602-06.

4355. Bowl of porcelain jasper from Grossalmerode in Hesse, mounted in filigree silver, c. 1675? The bowl belonged to Queen Charlotte Amalie, sister of the Landgrave Carl of Hesse.

4361. One of originally 6 cups and saucers of jasper. Italy or Løhlbach in Hesse.

4373. Standing cup and cover with stem in the shape of a Moor riding on a dragon. Gold enamel, set with cameos and intaglios of ancient gods, emperors and of European rulers. The individual cameo or intaglio was much prized as an art form during the Renaissance, when the ancient art of stonecutting was revived. After 1600 the use of carved stones as decorations on objects became the fashion, leading to a serial production of the craft. The colours, flowers and exotic fruits of the enamel date the goblet to 1635-50. (The figure of the Moor from c. 1610). The enamelling possibly done in The Netherlands, the stone-cutting in Prague, although the place of origin is unknown. The goblet, which belonged to the Duchess Frederikke Amalie of Holstein-Gottorp, was found at Gottorp Palace in 1734 and restored by the court Jeweller Frederik (I) Fabritius. Entered the Green Cabinet in 1736.

From the back wall above the 4th shelf from the top. (especially miniature portraits):

4377. The Landgrave Carl of Hesse (1654-1730). Relief of semi-precious stone in brass frame with his monogram and motto on the back. The relief ascribed to Francesco Mugniai, Cassel 1701-10.

4378.-4379. William III of England (1650-1702) and Mary (1662-1695). Miniatures.

4380.-4381. Prince George (1653-1708) and Queen Anne (1665-1714) of Great Britain. Enamel signed by Charles Boit, 1705 and 1705.

4382. Frederik III and Sophie Amalie; engraved mother-of-pearl inlaid in slate, made by Jeremias Hercules? The Queen's portrait was not included in the Green Cabinet, and is not a pendant to the King's since she is reproduced in a larger format.

4383.-4384. Christian IV and Kirsten Munk. Gouaches signed by Jacob van Doordt 1623. Sketches for now lost parade portraits; the King is wearing his coronation side-rapier (no.3655).

4385. Queen Charlotte Amalie in triumphal chariot. Engraved mother-of-pearl, inlaid in slate. Made by Jeremias Hercules?

4386. The royal coat-of-arms. Enamel, signed by Josias Barbette, 1694.

4387. Louis the Pious of France (1215-70). Enamel by Paul Prieur? In 1718 believed to depict Christian I, the first of the Oldenborg kings.

4388. Christian IV 1611. Miniature ascribed to Jacob van Doordt; locket made by Paul Kurtz 1656?

4389. Christian IV 1616. Miniature ascribed to Jacob van Doordt.

4390. Queen Anne Cathrine 1612. Miniature ascribed to Jacob van Doordt; contemporary locket of gold enamel.

4391. Christian IV 1638-40. Miniature. Locket Danish?

4392. The Electress Anna of Brandenburg (1576-1625). On the back her husband Johan Siegmund (1572-1619), brother of Queen Anne Cathrine. Miniature in oil from 1612. Believed in 1718 to depict the Duchess Elisabeth of Brunswick, sister of Christian IV.

4393. Christian IV 1645. Miniature in oil, by Karel van Mander? After losing an eye at the Battle of Kolberger Heide in 1644, the King only allowed himself to be shown in profile.

4394. Christian, the Prince Elect 1642-43. Miniature in oil, by Karel van Mander?

4395. Christian IV 1640. Miniature in oil, by Karel van Mander?

4396. Christian IV 1645. Miniature in oil, by Karel van Mander?

4397. Frederik III, c. 1645. Miniature in oil, by Karel van Mander? Frederik III became heir to the throne only after the death of his brother, the Prince Elect, in 1647, but he had himself painted with a hair plait, characteristic of Christian IV.

4398.-4399. Christian V and Queen Charlotte Amalie 1672. Miniatures signed by Louis Goullon; lockets by Paul Kurtz?

4400.-4402. The Electress Anna Sophie of Saxony (1647-1717), Queen Ulrika Eleonora of Sweden (1656- 93) and the Electress Wilhelmine Ernestine of Pfalz (1650-1706), Christian V's sisters, 1680. Miniatures by Louis Goullon.

4403. Prince George, Christian V's brother, 1674. Miniature by Louis Goullon.

4404. Queen Anne of Great Britain, Wife of Prince George, 1680s. Miniature

4405.-4406. Christian V and Queen Charlotte Amalie 1670. Miniatures signed by Maria Augustine Duchastel.

4407. Duchess Frederikke Amalie of Holstein-Gottorp (1649-1704), Christian V's sister, 1680. Miniature by Louis Goullon.

4408. The royal coat-of-arms; on the back Christian V's monogram. Enamel medallion by Josias Barbette, 1696-97.

4409. Princesse Sophie Hedvig (1677-1735), Christian V's daughter, c. 1695. Enamel by Josias Barbette.

4410. The Adoration of the Shepherds. Relief of oak, dated 1633, in later medallion of tortoiseshell and brass.

4411. Princess Sophie Hedvig. Miniature, variant of 409.

4423.-4424. Two knife handles of blue glass, mounted in silver gilt. Made by Christian Albrecht Kunckel at Christianhavn's Glassworks or by Francois Augier at the glassworks behind the Stock Exchange, 1690-92

4427. Knife handle of girasole, mounted in silver gilt. Belonged to Leonora Christina; confiscated by Frederik III 1661 (nr. 4155).

From the top shelf:

4435. Cup of black jade with dragon handle, mounted in filigree gold with turquoises, rubies, emeralds and rock crystal. The cup was carved in Samarkand c. 1425-50, or in Turkey c. 1600; the mounting is Ottoman. Belonged to Christian, the Prince Elect.

4440. Lekytos of onyx. The pitcher presumably dates from antiquity; the gold mounting from 17th cent. Belonged to Leonora Christina.

4441. Jewel box with Biblical figures. Agate inlaid in enamelled gold with rubies. South Germany, c. 1600.

4442. Standing cup of lapis lazuli; on the cover a gold figure of Pallas Athene. Cover and foot carved by Francesco Tortorino, Milan 1550-1600; body turned in South Germany?

4443. Mussel-shaped standing cup of jade, mounted in enamelled gold. The Miseroni studio in Milan c. 1580.

4444. Standing cup and cover of agate jasper mounted in silver gilt enamel. Hans Jakob Mair or Heinrich Mannlich, Augsburg, c. 1680 (no. 5180).

4446. Jade bowl with snake handle and tortoise foot of enamelled gold. From c. 1640.

4448. Pot of white jade with cover of filigree gold enamel with pearls and emeralds. Pot from Samarkand, 1425-50? Mounting Danish, c. 1600. Belonged to Kirsten Munk. Confiscated from her daughter, Leonora Christina, by Frederik III 1661 and given to Queen Sophie Amalie.

4450. Standing cup and cover of agate, mounted in gold enamel with rubies and a diamond. Cover carved with the four fields of the Württemberg arms. As cover finial a warrior with Duke Johann Friederich's arms and title. On the stem signature HK 1620 for Hans (Johann) Kobenhaupt, Stuttgart. Presumably a gift from the Duke, Christian IV's brother-in-law. Donated as a carrousel riding prize by Queen Sophie Amalie in 1680 and won by Christian V.

4451. Bowl of porphyry from Helgeland, south of Trondheim, which Christian V passed through on his 4,500 km royal progress through Norway in 1685. Carved by Denis Piengart, who was sent to Norway to search for minerals in 1688.

4452. Bowl of stone from the River Gave with inlaid ornamentation and angel mask in gold. Carved by Master Benedict in Navarre before 1555; presumably presented to Frederik II together with the Order of St Michael in 1559.

4456. Nautilus cup with carved reliefs of Frederik III and Sophie Amalie and their arms, 1666-1670.

4458. Tazza of agate jasper in silver gilt with garnets. The dragons of the handles and the auricular ornamentation of the foot date the cup to 1640-50.

4463. Standing cup and cover of Bohemian agate from Turnov (Kozákov). The gold enamel mounting on the cover made in Prague, c. 1580? The rings on the foot and stem, set with garnets, are repairs from before 1718.

4465. Tureen of gold enamel, set with cameos and intaglios; on the handles Moors' heads with pearl wreaths. Prague or The Nederlands, c. 1650? Presumably belonged to Queen Charlotte Amalie.

4466. Octagonal casket of partly enamelled gold, set with cameos, intaglios and semi-precious stones. In the lid rock crystal with engraved winter landscape. Northern Europe, c. 1650.

4467. Salt of jaspis, mounted in silver gilt with head of a Turk, a female and a bacchus figure with mother-of-pearl and pearls. Central Europe, 1630-50?

4472. Woman's head. Back of the head of Saxon serpentine, face partly of silver and enamel gilt. Saxony 1635-50? Drinking bowl, possibly reliquary holder with a new cover?

From the wall above the bottom of the cupboard
(especially miniature portraits and intaglios).

4473. Frederik III. Enamel, signed Paul Prieur 1663. The portrait
is a masterpiece, since the enamel's melting point limits both
the number of colours and the size of the miniature.
4474.-4475. Frederik III and Queen Sophie Amalie. Miniatures by
Alexander Cooper 1655; the gold enamel lockets from 1656
by Paul Kurtz?
4476. Frederik III. Enamel by Paul Prieur, c. 1660.
4477. Queen Sophie Amalie 1680. Miniature by Louis Goullon.
4478.-4481. Christian V as Crown Prince and Princesses Anna
Sophie, Frederikke Amalie and Wilhelmine Ernestine,
1655. Belong with nos. 4474-4475.
4482. Queen Ulrike Eleonora of Sweden, 1680. Miniature by
Pierre Signac.
4483. Frederik III's five eldest children, including Crown Prince
Christian (V), 1652. Enamel after an extinct painting, signed
by Paul Prieur 1671.
4484. Queen Sophie Amalie. Enamel by Paul Prieur, c. 1660.
4485. Unknown woman. Miniature, c. 1680.
4486. Frederik III. Miniature, 1650s.
4487. Frederik III. Enamel by Paul Prieur, 1660s.
4488.-4489. Sophie Amalie as Dowager Queen and Queen Ulrika
Eleonora of Sweden, 1680. Miniatures by Louis Goullon.
Mounted in lockets set with diamonds to attach on bracelets.
4490.-4491. Christian V and Queen Charlotte Amalie. Enamels by
Josias Barbette, c. 1690?
4492. Princess Sophie Hedevig, Christian V's daughter. Enamel,
signed by Josias Barbette 1693.
4493. Charles I of Great Britain (1600-49). Miniature in locket of
gold enamel; on the back a skull and crossbones. Charles
was beheaded in 1649 and was soon considered a martyr,
especially after the restoration of the monarchy in 1660. He
was the nephew of Christian IV.
4494. Charles II of Great Britain (1630-85). Miniature in gold enamel locket, dated 1660.
4495. James II of Great Britain (1633-1701). Miniature, signed by
Susan Rosse, c. 1685.
4496.-4497. Louis XIV of France (1638-1715. Two enamels by Jean
Petitot.
4499.-4500. Christian V. Enamels, signed by Paul Prieur 1674 and
Josias Barbette 1693.
4501. Michael Korybut Wisniowiecki (1638-73), King of Poland.
Enamel, signed by Paul Prieur, 1670.

4502. Queen Christina of Sweden (1626-89) in Rome. Miniature by Pierre Signac.

4503. Lady Castlemaine (1641-1709), Charles II's mistress. Enamel, signed by Paul Prieur 1669. Pendant to no. 4498.

4504.-4505. The Landgrave Wilhelm VI of Hesse (1629-63) and the Landgravine Hedvig Sophie (1623-83), Queen Charlotte Amalie's parents. Miniatures. By Karel van Mander?

4506. The Elector Friedrich Wilhelm of Brandenburg (1620-88), Queen Charlotte Amalie's uncle. Enamel.

4507. Gustavus II Adolphus of Sweden (1594-1632) on horseback. Cameo. On the back a lion and the motto: Cum deo et victribus armis; with God and the victorious arms. Nuremberg, 1632?

4508. Christoph Berent van Galen, Prince-bishop of Münster (1606-78). Miniature in oil. By Karel van Mander? Van Galen was Denmark's ally during the Scanian War.

4509.-4510. Carl X Gustav of Sweden (1622-1660) and Queen Hedvig Eleonora (1636-1715). Miniatures in oil. By Karel van Mander?

4511. Carl XI of Sweden (1655-1697). Miniature by Elias Brenner, presumably a gift at the king's wedding to Princess Ulrika Eleonora in 1680.

4526. Intaglio of cornelian. Woman's head, flanked by two double profiles with another head between the noses; in the hair 5 bearded male heads.

4536. Cameo of onyx with 3 faces, mounted in gold ring with enamel and diamonds; inside: Bollamin Killigrew. Possibly a gift from Captain Killigrew, whose father ran a theatre in London which Crown Prince Christian (V) attended during his travels abroad in 1662? Killigrew made pitchers of stoneware called »bellarmines«, hence his nickname Bollamin.

4545. »Justice on a Monument«. Intaglio of sardonyx mounted in gold.

4558. Cross of the Order of the Dannebrog, sceptre, apple and sword and the three crowns of the Kalmar Union. Intaglio of topaz, mounted in a gold signet ring by Paul Kurtz. Used by Christian V at his anointment in 1671.

4563. Pallas Athene. Intaglio of sardonyx, mounted in portrait locket of silver gilt.

4571. Mars? Intaglio of sardonyx mounted in gold.

4589. Christian V. Intaglio of chalcedony. Denmark, 1670s.

4596. Signet ring of cornelian mounted in silver. Turkey.

4600. Ring of agate with Cupid blowing soap bubbles, and the inscription: Comme les amis du temps. The ring belonged to Duke Christian Albrecht of Holstein-Gottorp and symbolizes the betrayal of friendship. Although married to Christian V's sister, Frederikke Amalie, Christian V banished him twice. His marriage was also unhappy.

4601. Ring of jade with crown of thorns and the motto: ad illam per hanc. For its owner, Duke Christian Albrecht of Holstein-Gottorp, a symbol of survival both religious – through suffering to salvation – and political – from banishment to restitution.

4606. Christian IV. Miniature in oil. Jacob van Doordt, c. 1610.

4607. Christian IV. Relief in wax, signed: DVHB 1648. Presumably posthumously, since the King is depicted *en face*. (cf no. 4393).

4608. Christian V crowned with laurels. Miniature in oil. Jacob d'Agar?

4609. Queen Sophie Amalie in peasant costume. Painted by Wolfgang Heimbach. The Queen was fond of court ballets. In one performance in 1655 she danced no fewer than 5 roles, including one in peasant costume, complete with egg basket, from Vierland, between Altona and Glückstad.

From the bottom of the cupboard.

Ten portrait medallions of ivory, all carved by Johann Heinrich Wessel in the 1680s.

4615.-4616. Iacob Massau, treasurer in Gottorp, and his wife, Anna Cathrine.

4617. Duke Christian Albrecht of Holstein-Gottorp (1641-94).

4618.-4619. Duchess Frederikke Amalie.

4620. Christian V.

4621. Duke Frederik IV of Holstein-Gottorp (1671-1702) as Crown Prince.

4623. Princess Sophie Amalie of Holstein-Gottorp (1670-1710)?

4624. The Elector Johann Georg III of Sachsen (1647-91)

4625. Unknown woman. Medallion of turned ivory; roughly executed, royal handicraft?

4626.-4627. Duke Christian Albrecht of Holstein-Gottorp. Two portrait medallions by Joachim Henne, 1660s.

4628. Unknown man. Wax relief in turned wooden box.

4633. The Elector Friederich Wilhelm of Brandenburg (1620-1688). Portrait box of ivory, signed: EE.

4645. Boy pulling a girl's plait. Ivory statuette. Joachim Henne, 1660s?

4648. Octagonal casket of ivory, with love scenes in silk patchwork. South Germany, c. 1630.

4649. Cabinet of ivory, engraved with gods, virtues and memento mori symbols. South Germany, c. 1600?

4650.-4651. Ivory casket containing two spoons in a chain carved of wood. The spoons symbolize marriage and faithfulness.

4653. Jewel box of ivory with figures and silver gilt mounting, in the lid a painted and engraved representation of musical putti. Goldsmith work by Daniel Zech in Augsburg, (d. 1657).

4654. Terrine with handle and feet in the shape of dolphins. Gold enamel, set with cameos and intaglios. The Netherlands or Prague, 1635-50? Provenance as no. 4374.

The staircase leads down to the Treasury

5000. Christian III's Sword of State. Grip and scabbard of gold with enamel and table-cut diamonds. Made in 1551 by the goldsmith Johann Siebe. After design by Jakob Binck? Before the introduction of Absolutism in 1660, the Sword of State was the first of the regalia to be handed over to the King. Used for the last time at the coronation of Frederik III in 1648.

5002. The Oldenborg Horn. Legend has it that in the year 989, the first member of the House of Oldenborg, Count Otto, while out hunting met a young maiden, who handed him a drinking horn and bade him drink his fill. He sensibly threw away the contents and kept the horn. The legend notwithstanding, the horn, made of silver decorated with enamel, was made in c. 1465 and was probably presented to Cologne Cathedral by Christian I. After the Reformation it was returned to the family's possession. In 1667 it was handed down from the ducal line of Oldenborg to the Danish Royal House.

5004. Relief in chased gold from the late 15th century representing St. Michael.

5006. St. George medallion of enamelled gold. On the reverse an added medallion of Joseph and Mary with the Child. Both from c. 1550 and both in the same frame of rubies and emeralds from the 17th century.

5008. Hat ornament, consisting of gold plate with beaten and chiselled female figure with vase in high relief. Pandora? Milan, c. 1560?

5010. Mirror in gilt, richly ornamented silver frame with garnets. Made in Antwerp c. 1565.

5012. Philip of Spain (1527-98). Onyx cameo with name. Made by Jacopo da Trezzo or his workshop in Madrid c. 1560.

5014. Gold medallion with beaten and chiselled portrayal of Christ on the Throne. On the reverse: CUR QVÆRIS NOMEN MEU. QUOD EST MIRABILE: You ask my name. It is wondrous. A reference to the angel's reply to the childless Manoah before his wife bears Samson. (Judges, 13) Amulet to ward of infertility? South Germany 1550-1600?

5016. Chalice of gold with inlaid enamel. Made for Frederik II's newly erected chapel at Kronborg by the goldsmith Hans Raadt in 1583?

5018. Paten of gold with inlaid enamel. Made in the latter half of the 16th century. From Kronborg Castle Chapel.

5020. The Order of the Elephant in its oldest existing form, with Frederik II's picture, monogram and motto. Made in 1580 by Hans Raadt after a drawing by Melchior Lorck?

5022. Chain of the Order of the Elephant, of quatrefoil rosettes.

5024.-5026. Two gold chains with rectangular links for pendants. c. 1600.

5027. Sweetmeat bowl of silver gilt, glorifying the Danish coat-of-arms borne by a lion. Made by Hinrich Lambrecht I, Hamburg c. 1600.

5028. The Order of the Mailed Sword-Arm, dated 1617. Gold enamel with table-cut stones. Instituted by Christian IV to commemorate the Kalmar War against Sweden 1611-13. Made by Corvinianus Sauer?

5030. The Order of the Elephant. Gold enamel with table-cut stones. On the elephant's cloth the Order of the Mailed Sword-Arm (no. 5028). This combination of the two orders was conferred on two occasions, in 1633 and 1634. Since then only the Order of the Elephant has been conferred.

5032. Silver plates with amber bases, made in 1585 in Königsberg by Andreas Knieffel for the Margravine Sophie of Brandenburg, née Princess of Brunswick and Lüneburg, Frederik II's cousin. Amberwork by Stenzel Snitt? Housewarming present to Frederik II at Kronborg?

5034. Wine jug of silver with Frederik II's crowned monogram: Fredericus Secundus. Danish work?

5036. Rosary of cornelians, onyx and gold beads, and scallop of garnet. 16th century.

5038. Knife handle of gold with monogram, in figures, of Queen Sophie and Frederik II.

5040. Gold spoon, engraved with Queen Sophie's monogram and coat-of-arms of Mecklenburg. Denmark, c. 1600?

5042. Knife handle with Queen Sophie's monogram and warrior with shield of gold on black enamel. Denmark, c. 1590?

5044. Pomander in the form of a skull, gold and white enamel with rubies. Sponge interior with six compartments for perfume. On a string with corals carved like skulls, of which two are with crown and smiling female face, symbolizing the transience of human life. Denmark, c. 1600.

5046. Queen Anne Cathrine's coat-of-arms as Princess of Brandenburg, embroidered with gold and pearls and studded with turquoises and garnets. From her bed canopy, part of her dowry in 1597.

5048.-5050. Two clothes brushes with silver gilt handles from 1597, with Queen Anne Cathrine's coat-of-arms and initials and her parents' monogram.

5052. Pendant in the form of a crowned lion, made in gold with blue enamel and diamonds, from c. 1600.

5054. Pendant in the form of a crowned lion, made in gold with brown enamel and gilded mounting with diamonds, from c. 1600.

5056. Reliefs in silver of Christian IV and Anne Cathrine. Made from designs by Jacob van Doordt, probably after the Queen's death in 1612.

5058. Bracelet of pierced enamelled gold (blue lions, heart with arrow) and the crowned letters A.C. for Queen Anne Cathrine. Beneath the arrow and monogram, braided hair. A gift from Christian IV to his wife?

5060. Bracelet with rubies and diamonds, the links in the form of hearts and hour glasses and the clasp a winged hourglass, symbolizing Love's victory over Death. On the back Christian IV's cipher in enamel. A gift to his mother, Queen Sophie.

5062. Gold cross with female figure (»Faith«) and necklace of enamelled gold with rubies, emeralds, a diamond and pearls. From c. 1590.

5064. Spoon with stem of heliotrope and gold enamel, bowl of conch-shell (cyprea tigris). From c. 1610. Whooping cough medicine was thought to have added effect when taken from a conch-shell.

5066. Book cover in gold and champlevé enamel; bears the coats-of-arms of Denmark, Schleswig and Holstein and the initials: A(ugsburg) G(eboren) A(us) K(öniglichem) S(tamm) Z(u) D(änemark) H(erzogin) Z(u) S(chleswig) H(olstein) and I(ohan) A(dolph) H(erzog) Z(u) S(chleswig) H(olstein) 1613.

5068. Cup of reddish-brown jasper made in Venice in the 14th century. The gold and enamel mounting orginates from Christian IV's time. In the bottom a K denoting Kirsten Munk?

5070. Handwritten prayer book belonging to Kirsten Munk and written by herself. On the first page the date, 22nd Sept 1617, written by the King. Later additions by Sophie Rantzau and Leonora Christina. On the cover figure monograms in enamel: 3.4.10.13. (i.e. C(hristian) IV K(irsten) M(unk).

5072. Handwritten prayer book. Belonged to Kirsten Munk. Enamelled ornaments with symbols of Evangelists, and a crowned

C K signifying Christian Kirsten. Inside are the names of Christian IV and his sons from 1625, and the name and handwriting of Corfitz Ulfeld's mother from 1636, to whom it must have belonged.

5074. Spoon of gold and enamel with a cut sapphire in the form of a leaf. Bears the letters C. K. (Christian Kirsten). Belonged to Kirsten Munk. Sapphires were called female sapphires and symbolized woman's fidelity.

5076. Signet ring with engraved sapphire with Christian IV's monogram and the coats-of-arms of the kingdom's provinces. The sapphire was cut in 1623, the ring, of gold and enamel, made in Hamburg in 1641.

5078. Rose-shaped ornament of enamelled gold with seven red stones. From c. 1600?

5080. Signet ring of gold and engraved sapphire with the Prince Elect's monogram and the coats-of-arms of state and the provinces. From c. 1625.

5082. Vinaigrette of gold with hunting scenes in glass enamel. From 1620-30.

5084.-5086. Insignia and garter of the Order of the Garter, sent to Frederik II by Elizabeth I in 1582. Gold and velvet with enamel, diamonds and rubies.

5088.-5094. Collar, the »Great« Insignia, Garter and »Lesser« Insignia of the Order of the Garter, sent to Christian IV by James I in 1603. Gold with enamel and diamonds, velvet with pearls and rubies. The collar and the Great Insignia, the latter mounted on a base as a statuette in c. 1650, were only worn on ceremonial occasions. They should have been returned on Christian IV's death in 1648, but were not, owing to the political instability in England. They were thus preserved, and are now thought to be the oldest examples in existence.

5096. Gold cup engraved with a crowned C4 and the date 1644. Made by Caspar Herbach?

5098. Butter bowl of dark-green Saxony serpentine with gold mounting on which is engraved: C4 Friedrichsburgk 1643. Made by Caspar Herbach?

5100. Gold spoon with Christian IV's crowned monogram in red enamel. Denmark, c. 1640?

5102. Hourglass of gold enamel with Christian IV's monogram, the year 1633 and a rebus consisting of a burning heart and the words Jahve (Hebrew for Jehovah) and Dirige meum: The Lord direct my burning heart. The rebus has parallels on the Round Tower and on coins from the 1640's.

5104. Sexfoil gold beaker with enamel, rubies and a sapphire. Made for the Prince Elect's wedding in 1634?

5106. Oval mirror, on the back of which Christian IV's rebus from the Round Tower with enamel letters on black velvet. (no. 5102)

5108. Sapphire in silver setting as costume ornament.

5110. Gustavus II Adolphus (1594-1632), King of Sweden. Relief portrait in gold and enamel, made after a medal by Sebastian Dadler. Nuremberg, 1630's?

5112. Spoon with bowl of enamelled gold and stem of coral. From c. 1620?

5114. Knife handle of gold with alchemistic inscription(?): 4 3/6 K and a crowned figure monogram 8 for the Electress Hedevig of Saxony, Christian IV's sister, and the date 1632.

5116. Butter bowl of stoneware with mounting of silver gilt. On the lid a Hebrew inscription for the Holy Trinity. On the foot a crowned 8 for the Electress Hedevig of Saxony and the date 1639. In Saxony, a dedicated development of stoneware production led to Meissen porcelain.

5118. Pair of gold scissors with figure of eight handle, Electress Hedevig's figure monogram and the year 1636.

5120. Forkhandle of gold in the form of a negro figure. Gold with enamel and rubies. From c. 1630.

5122. Chalice, paten, wafer box and altar jug of gold with engraving in niello, white and black enamel, sapphires and diamonds. Made for Christian IV's sister, Duchess Augusta of Holstein-Gottorp, partly reusing precious stones from her mother's estate. The engraving on the chalice is based on illustrations by Matthæus Merian in 1625-28 for the Strasbourg edition of Luther's Bible in 1630.

5124. Christian IV's crown, made 1595-96 by the goldsmith Dirich Fyring in Odense. Gold with enamel, table-cut stones and pearls. The enamelled figures on the crown's large points illustrate the virtues which a good king should possess, and at the same time his functions as a sovereign: Starting at the front Caritas (a mother with a nursing child: the King as head of the Church, his love to God and to his subjects), Fortitudo (the woman sitting on a lion: courage and strength, the King as war lord), and Justitia (woman with sword and scales: righteousness, the King as judge). Between these, the pelican which pecks at its breast in order to feed its young with its own blood: originally a symbol of Christ's martyrdom, but here a symbol of the King's duty to protect and defend his people with his very blood.

The insides of the points show the coats-of-arms of the royal provinces. The present black-enamelled coats-of-arms were added for Frederik III's coronation in 1648, after Denmark had been forced to cede Gotland and Oesel at the Peace Treaty of 1645. Their coats-of-arms can be seen in the circlet of coloured shields that must be the originals. Also visible is the coat-of-arms of the Kalmar-Union with three open crowns, which can explain the crown's open form. The usual European closed crown with the points meeting in arches (as in the Absolutist crown no. 5592) was also the most common in Christian IV's time. By choosing an open crown like that used by the kings of the Union, Christian IV was stating that he was the heir to a united North. The crown was used for the last time at Frederik III's coronation in 1648. For this occasion an inset section of arches was made, as can be seen in the miniature portrait of Frederik III (no. 5174), so as to close the crown. It was probably melted down and used again when Christian V had the Absolutist crown made in 1670-71.

5126. Pendants with monogram in enamelled metal, used as presents and in remembrance of the deceased. From c. 1650.

5128. Octofoil chalice of gold with enamelled painting. On the cup the eight virtues, inside eight symbols with references from the Sermon on the Mount. In the bottom, an angel overcoming Death. On the foot, animals, underneath flowers and signature for the Nuremberg painter Georg Strauch 1648. Made for Frederik III's coronation the same year?

5130. A square piece of jade in a silver frame; with the inscription: 1648, 28th February, King Christian IV died with this gold chain round his neck and the stone therein. Jade was believed to protect its bearer against kidney stones.

5132. Two gold bracelets with reliefs showing the seasons and enamelled floral ornaments with diamonds. Wedding presents from Christian IV to his daughter-in-law Sophie Amalie in 1643. Made in Hamburg (no. 5540)?

5134. Prayerbook written by Christian IV and Kirsten Munk's daughter, Anne Cathrine, in the year of her death 1633. Cover of gold and enamel with naturalistic flowers, memento mori motifs and Biblical quotations. On the locks, Anne Cathrine's monogram, on the back her coats-of-arms as Duchess of Schleswig and Holstein. Made in Copenhagen c. 1648 (like no. 5534)?

5136. Oval box of gold with flower paintings in enamel. From c. 1650.

5138. Knife with sheath. Relief-work of gold with enamelled naturalistic flowers, animals and insects, studded with precious stones. Denmark, c. 1650?

5140. Shaving brush with enamelled gold handle, studded with table-cut diamonds and emeralds. Denmark, c. 1650?

5142. Knife handle of gold, cast and chiselled, with flowers. Denmark, c. 1650?

5144. Knife handle of gold with marine animal's head and table-cut stones. Denmark, before 1650?

5146. Case of gold with engravings of flowers, containing knife with gold handle. Denmark, c. 1650?

5148. French almanac from 1647 in a cylinder of enamelled gold. Brought back from Paris by Leonora Christina?

5150. Enamelled clasp for a chain, with initials C.V.F. for Corfitz Ulfeldt.

5152. Jug of gold, engraved with naturalistic flowers and studded with diamonds and rubies in grain enamel. Under the spout an engraved crowned MS for Magdalena Sibylla, the Prince Elect's widow, and the date 1650. Made by her court goldsmith in Nykøbing, Henrik Langmack?

5154. The Emperor Ferdinand III (1637-1657). Cameo of conchshell with name and coat-of-arms in a frame of enamelled flowers. After a medal by Georg Schweigger, Vienna c. 1650.

5156.-5160. Three gold cups with Frederik III's monogram and the Holstein arms in enamel. In the bottom a Hamburg gold »daler« (coin). Like (nos. 503, 2111 and 5162) made for a projected acclamation to Frederik III in Hamburg in 1654?

5162. Frederik III's so-called coronation cup. Nos. 5156-60, 503 and 2111 made for a projected acclamation to Frederik III in Hamburg in 1654? Signed by H. C. Brechtel in The Hague 1653.

5164. Tankard of gold embossed with pastoral scenes. Cover medallion with Orpheus playing for the animals, and knob in the form of a bagpiper in enamel. From the 1650's.

5166. Gold case with Frederik II's crowned monogram, containing scissors, razor, etc. From the 1650's.

5168. Covered cup of gold with the arms of the three Nordic kingdoms, F3 and 1669 in enamel. Inside, 12 tumblers to fit inside each other. Possibly made for Frederik III's 60th birthday, by Paul Kurtz?

5170. Pince-nez and case of gold, belonging to Duke Frederik III of Holstein-Gottorp (1597-1659).

5172. Medallion, in a piece of Frederik III's »Tree of Life«, the only one of those belonging to Christian IV's three sons which thrived. On the obverse in enamel a tree with the inscription: Non sine omine ex tribus superstes. (Not without omen shall you survive of three.)

5174.-5176. Frederik III and Sophie Amalie wearing coronation robes, 1648. Frederik III is wearing Christian IV's crown converted into a closed crown with arches (no. 5124). Miniatures in oil, unknown artist.

5178. Toilet mirror in enamelled frame with agates and masks. South Germany, c. 1670.

5180.-5182. Two jewel cases of silver and agate with enamelled flowers and set with stones. Made by Hans Jakob Mair in Augsburg, c. 1680.

5184. Two elephants of rock crystal, bought by Frederik III in Hamburg in 1652.

5186. Crucifix, enamelled and gilded, with the inscription: Wachset printz zu hohen fürsten Ehren. Ehre Jahr und Glück sich stets vermeren.

5188. Jutland-style pot in gold and enamel. Belonged to Frederik III.

5190. Gold spoon.

5192. Pendant. Enamelled, crowned trefoil with heart, figure rebus and monograms for the Elector Carl of Pfalz and his wife, Vilhelmine Ernestine, daughter of Frederik III. Wedding present from 1671; made by Paul Kurtz?

5194. Enamelled gold plate with the Lüneburg horse surrounded by the Danish and Lüneburg coats-of-arms, and two shields with Frederik III and Sophie Amalie's crowned monogram. Made by Paul Prieur c. 1670?

5196. Sophie Amalie's signet with disc of topaz and enamelled gold handle in the form of the Lüneburg horse. Made by Paul Kurtz, 1671.

5198. Frederik III's signet with disc of pale violet onyx and handle of enamelled flowers. Made by Paul Kurtz c. 1665?

5200. Sophie Amalie's signet with crown-shaped handle of gold filigree work.

5202.-5206. Gold cutlery with Frederik III's monogram in enamel: Spoon with fluted bowl from the 1650's, fork and spoon with lobed stems from the 1660's. Made by Paul Kurtz?

5208.-5210. Knife-handle and fork of gold with Sophie Amalie's enamelled monogram. Denmark, c. 1650 and 1660. Made by Paul Kurtz?

5212. Watch with floral enamel. On the lid an antique cameo with Ganymede on the eagle in a ring of rubies. The works signed: Nicolaus Rugendas. Aug(sburg).

5214. Watch with enamelled representation of Venus and Adonis. works signed: Georg Cameel in Strasbourg, from c. 1650-60.

5216. Gold clock with embossed hunting scenes. Works signed: Johan Oldenburg, Hamburg. From the second half of the 17th century.

5218. Watch with gold filigree and flower enamel set with diamonds. Works signed: J. Thuret a Paris, from c. 1660.

5220. The Danish coat-of-arms with Collars of Orders and savages, of enamelled silver. Made by Josie Barbette c. 1690?

5222. Badge of the Order of the Elephant. Model with imitation stone, made before the final design of the badge was determined in 1679 (no. 5546). Made by Paul Kurtz?

5224.-5228. »The Order of the Mailed Sword-Arm«. Three enamelled badges with Christian V's monogram, one with diamonds. Prototypes for a projected revival of Christian IV's order. Made by Paul Kurtz?

5230.-5232. Two reliefs in gold with portraits of Christian V, made with hair braid like his great ideal, Christian IV, his grandfather (no. 202). Prototypes of projected medals? One of them belonged to Peder Griffenfeld.

5234.-5236. Two costume ornaments with rose quartz, set in gold with Christian V's monogram in enamel. Denmark, 1670's. Made by Paul Kurtz?

5238. Miniature Order of the Elephant, the tower of which is made into a whistle. Christian V's characteristic during hunts in the Deer Park, north of Copenhagen. Paul Kurtz, 1670's.

5240. Badge and Garter of the Order of the Garter, set with table-cut stones, presented to Christian V in 1662 when he was in England as Crown Prince.

5242. Case of gold with flowers, pierced and engraved. From c. 1675?

5244. Vinaigrette of gold (»Pilgrim's Flask«) with Christian V and Queen Charlotte Amalie's monogram.

5246. Knife handle representing a figure with a turban, enamelled gold set with diamonds. From c. 1675?

5248. Watch in case of gold filigree, signed Johan Stamhart. Late 17th century.

5250. Notebook of ivory with gold filigree, with Christian V's crowned monogram inside.

5252. Box of gold filigree with corals. From c. 1675?

5254. Head of garnet, enamelled and studded with diamonds, for pedestal. From c. 1675?

5256. Bust of a man in coral on enamelled pedestal. The bust Italian from c. 1600, the pedestal from Paris c. 1665?

5258. Female head of topaz on enamelled pedestal with precious stones.

5260. Gold medal with the Princesses Sophie Hedevig and Louise, Christian V's daughter and daughter-in-law, symbolized on the reverse by two pearls of equal beauty. Made for their joint birthday, 28.8.1699 by Anthon Meybusch. The last of Christian V's many medals.

5262.-5268. Basin, pitcher and two candlesticks of gold, used since 1671 at the christening of the Royal children. Until 1796, the names of father and child, date and time of birth were engraved, first underneath the basin and, from 1750, on the attached plate. The decorations are without religious content, as for example, the chased putti seasons on the basin. Is the christening set an original toilet set made by the Hamburg master Hinrich Lambrecht II, c. 1650?

5270. The Royal Statutes (the constitution of absolute monarchy 1665-1849), in a silver case with Frederik III's monogram and the date: 1665 14 Novembris. The King's private copy, kept with the regalia, while the one produced during the anointings is in the National Archives.

5272. Eight silver boxes with monogram and year, containing the umbilical cords of Frederik III's children, believed to provide protection against disease and death.

5274. Silver box with Frederik III's monogram, containing his unbroken fetal membrane, or caul, believed to bring strength and victory.

5276.-5278. Two flower pieces painted by Princess Sophie Hedevig and given to her brother Frederik IV on his 50th birthday in 1721. The King's monogram is balanced by the mirror, and is an invitation to moderation, since the King married Anna Sophie Reventlow the day after the death of Queen Louise, and crowned her Queen. Silver gilt frames with enamel and stones made by the Copenhagen master Niels Jonsen.

5280. Dish made of a hollowed-out garnet with gilded silver mountings. In the lid, Princess Sophie Hedevig's monogram, carved by Johann Christian Jönsch in 1731.

5282. Gilded and enamelled silver box with plates of agate, pearls and precious stones. Made by J.Chr.Köhler in Dresden, c. 1700.

5284.-5286. Two statuettes with Bacchus on a barrel of gilded silver with diamonds and pearls. Germany, c. 1700?

5288. Small covered bowl and two flagons of gold with enamel and diamonds, made by Johan Melchior Dinglinger in Dresden, c. 1700.

5290. The Russian Order of St. Andreas, of enamelled gold with diamonds. Given to Frederik IV by Peter the Great.

5292. Collared swan (the arms of Stormarn), formed of a single pearl with enamel and rose-cut diamond, sitting on two pearl eggs in a basket of gold. Belonged to Princess Charlotte Amalie, daughter of Frederik IV.

5294. Miniature altar built up of the symbols of the Passion of Christ, made in gold and enamel. In the centre an aquamarine.

5296. Lamb, made of a single pearl with rose-cut diamond and enamel mounting. From c. 1700.

5298. Frederik IV. Head carved in clear onyx.

5300. Miniature altar of silver gilt, with Biblical scenes, set with enamel figures and rose-cut diamonds. From c. 1700.

5302. Gold tumbler from c. 1700.

5304.-5306. Two travelling beakers of gold with engraved decoration, Frederik IV's mirror monogram and the royal coat-of-arms. From c. 1730.

5308. Gold cup with Frederik IV's monogram in diamonds. A present to the coming Chancellor, Count U.A. Holstein, Anna Sophie's brother-in-law, who had aided Frederik IV at her abduction from Clausholm.

5310.-5318. Beakers, two tumblers and two covered beakers of gold with Frederik IV's crowned mirror monogram in enamel. The covered cups stamped with the master mark of Frederik (I) Fabritius, 1730.

5320.-5324. Three gold writing sets with respectively Princess Sophie Hedevig, Frederik IV and Christian VI's monograms. The last mentioned made by Frederik (I) Fabritius, c. 1730.

5326. Box of gold for spices. On the lid Frederik IV's mirror monogram in enamel.

5328.-5332. Travelling cutlery: knife, spoon and fork of gold and Frederik IV's mirror monogram in enamel.

5334. Case of silver gilt from c. 1720. Inside strips of ivory with signature Charles. Frederik IV's brother, Prince Carl?

5336. Toilet set of silver with enamel, and with the Copenhagen silversmith Marcus Pipgros' stamp 1729. Enamel work by Pierre Fromery in Berlin?

5338. Six cups with Chinese figures in gold on white enamel from c. 1720.

5340. Vase of silver gilt with enamel and rose-cut diamonds. Dresden, c. 1710.

5342. Oval box with Chinese figures in gold on white enamel. From c. 1720.

5344. Walking stick of tortoiseshell, knob with Chinese figures in gold on enamel and ring of precious stones. From c. 1730.

5346. Walking stick of tortoiseshell, knob of gold with Chinese figures. From c. 1730.

5348. Walking stick of cane, knob of enamelled gold and rose-cut diamonds. On the top Frederik IV's mirror monogram. The enamelling done by his sister, Princess Sophie Hedevig.

5350. Walking stick of tortoiseshell with knob of gold. On the top an enamelled motto: Mes Mouvements sont cachés (My movements are bound).

5352. Walking stick of cane with knob of gold, diamonds and crowned double F. Belonged to Frederik IV.

5354. Christian VI's accolade rapier with hilt of enamelled gold and diamonds. From c. 1730.

5356. Walking stick of narwhal tusk with gold knob. Belonged to Christian VI.

5358. Walking stick of cane, handle of onyx with gold mounts from c. 1750. Probably belonged to Frederik V.

5360. Repeating clock in case of agate with gold mounting. The clock signed: J.Faver, London. Added chatelaine of agate and tombac. Matching no. 5358?

5362. Hinged chatelaine with sewing box and two pomanders of onyx with mounting of gilded tombac. Bought in 1841 by Christian VIII. Matching no. 5358?

5364. Clock with chatelaine of gold with jasper, diamonds and rubies. Clock signed: D.Hubert, London. Present from Christian VI to Sophie Magdalene.

5366.-5372. Four gold pins with crown-shaped handles studded with rose-cut diamonds and:
Sapphire. Present to Queen Sophie Magdalene from her father-in-law, Frederik IV.
Portrait of the young Christian VI under diamond. The portrait was probably done by H.J. Pohle, the pin by Frederik (I) Fabritius in 1723.
Heart-shaped emerald, cut by Sophie Hedevig and donated by Sophie Magdalene.
Portrait of Christian VI under rock crystal. Belonged to his sister, Princess Charlotte Amalie.

5374. A pair of earrings with small brilliants in silver fringe, with pear-shaped rose-cut diamond pendants and black agates to match. The rose-cut diamonds on top were presumably added later. Belonged to Sophie Magdalene.

5376. The Order »de l'union parfaite«, instituted in 1732 by Sophie Magdalene to commemorate her happy marriage, and which she conferred until her death; the first order in Denmark which could also be worn by women.

5378. A pair of earrings with pear-shaped rose-cut diamonds. Belonged to Christian VI's sister, Princess Charlotte Amalie.

5380. Gold clock with chatelaine studded with diamonds, lapis lazuli and moss agate. Signed: (Jean-Baptiste) Hervé, Paris. Mentioned in Sophie Magdalene's will 1746.

5382. Gold clock signed Ferdinand Engelschalck, Prague c. 1720. On the works a crowned mirror monogram GR for George I of England?

5384. Oval box of gold studded with rose-cut diamonds, from c. 1730.

5386. Mirror in gold frame, ornamented with precious stones, enamel and miniatures, including one of Paris and the Three Graces. Back and legs veneered with tortoiseshell and ivory. Augsburg, 1710-20?

5388. Sophie Magdalene's medicine chest, covered with tortoiseshell and mother-of-pearl. Made in Naples in 1731 by I. Sarao.

5390. Gold case with knife, pencil-holder, earpick, bodkin, glove buttons and compass. From c. 1730.

5392. Chocolate cup with cover. Gilt enamelled silver with Chinese figures in gold. France, c. 1740. Belonged to Sophie Magdalene. Matching teaspoon of gold.

5394.-5396. Two gold boxes with inlaid medallions, made by H.J. Schrader in 1753. On the outside, relief of Queen Louise on blue enamel, made after M.G. Arbien's coronation medal from 1746. Inside enamelled landscape. The boxes made by court jeweller Christopher Fabritius?

5398. Heart-shaped vinaigrette of gold with Frederik V's monogram.

5400. Watch in locket of gold with enamelled flowers. From c. 1760.

5402. Vinaigrette of enamelled gold representing a shepherdess with a dog. Made by Nathaniel Falchengreen in Copenhagen, 1757.

5404. Gold box; in the lid, a relief in mother-of-pearl with portraits of the first twelve kings of the House of Oldenborg. Made after M.G. Arbiens medal commemorating the 300 years jubilee of the Royal House, 1749.

5406. Gold clock; on the dial relief portaits of the first twelve kings of the House of Oldenborg. Made in Copenhagen by the watchmaker Pierre Charlo in the mid-18th century.

5408. Sundial of partly gilt and enamelled silver, containing a spirit level, compass, perpetual calender and inscriptions by A. Holm. Present to Frederik V on the occasion of the 300 years jubilee of the Royal House in 1749?

5410. The Eider Cup of gold, made by Nicolai Langermann, 1751. Mounted plates with inscriptions and reliefs commemorating the Treaty of Frederiksborg in 1720 and the coronation of Queen Anna Sophie in 1721. The plates were made by Peter Klein and originate from a book binding, a 50th birthday present to Frederik IV from Anna Sophie Reventlow in 1721.

5412. Cup of Allegiance of gold, made by Nicolai Langermann in 1756. Mounted plates with inscriptions and reliefs commemorating Frederik IV's 50th birthday and the Pledge of Allegiance by the Schleswig Assembly in 1721. The plates were made by Peter Klein and originate from a book binding, a 50th birthday present to Frederik IV from Anna Sophie Reventlow in 1721.

5414. Covered cup of gold with inlaid medals of Frederik IV, Prince Jørgen and Queen Louise. Copenhagen, c. 1750.

5416. Agate box mounted with chased gold and studded with brilliants. France, c. 1740?

5418. The Insignia of the Order of the Elephant, set with diamonds, rubies and sapphires, and Frederik V's monogram. Made for Prince Frederik, the Heir Presumptive, by J.F. Fistaine, 1772?

5420. Octagonal Bohemian topaz with intaglio portrait of Frederik V, carved by Lorenz Natter in 1757. Signed.

5426. Box of jasper and gold with rubies and brilliants; curved triangular shape. Made in Copenhagen by the French jeweller J.F. Fistaine in 1761.

5428. Tureen of blue-enamelled and gilt silver, ornamented with biscuitware reliefs after antique cameos. Made in Copenhagen, c. 1755, by Nicolai Langemann.

5430. Tureen of blue-enamelled and gilt silver (as no. 5428) with portraits in relief of Queen Juliane Marie's relatives in Brunswick, made by J.E. Bauert in 1755.

5432. Oval gold box. In the lid, relief of Frederik V carved in Icelandic agate. Copenhagen, c. 1766.

5434. Gold box with miniature of Queen Juliane Marie surrounded with diamonds, painted by W.A. Müller c. 1780.

5436. Gold coffee and tea service, made by Th.A. Westrup in Copenhagen 1761-62 for the Lord High Steward, Count Adam Gottlob Moltke, friend of Frederik IV. (No. 5438 also belongs to this.)

5438. Twelve teaspoons and sugar tongs of gold from the mid-18th century. (Belongs to no. 5436).

5440. Necklace of river pearls with clasp of brilliants. According to tradition, this was presented to Queen Caroline Mathilde by Scottish women at her departure for Denmark in 1766. Inherited in the Ducal family of Augustenborg.

5442. A pair of earrings in rock crystal with yellow topaz pendants. Belonged to Caroline Mathilde.

5444. Watch in pierced locket, with wreath and crown of rubies and diamonds, believed to be a present from Caroline Mathilde.

5446. Brooch, originally a ring, with Cape ruby and diamonds in a gold setting. Belonged to Count Marcus Gerhard Rosencrone.

5448. Christian VII, relief portrait in diamonds, presented to the King by the goldsmiths of Paris, 1768.

5450. Box of gold for the King's diploma of the Freedom of the City of London. Made by John Harvey. Allegorical reliefs on the lid signed: G.M. Moser fecit 1769.

5452. Seal from the King's diploma as Honorary Doctor of Oxford University.

5454. Box of gold for the King's diploma as Honorary Member of the Goldsmiths' Guild in London. Made by John Harvey in London.

5456. Enamelled gold box with »Capitoline doves« in mosaic. Belonged to Catharina II of Russia.

5458. »Souvenir case« of enamelled metal with gold mounting. Inside pen and strips of ivory with inscription by Prince Frederik, the Heir Presumptive. Denmark, c. 1780.

5460. Chatelaine of gold with enamel miniatures, from c. 1770.

5462. »Souvenir case« of gold with green enamel, made by Frederik (II) Fabritius c. 1780, with miniature portraits of Prince Frederik, the Heir Presumptive and his consort, painted by Cornelius Høyer.

5464. »Souvenir case« of metal with gold mounting and miniature portraits of Juliane Marie and Prince Frederik, the Heir Presumptive. From c. 1780.

5466. »Souvenir case« of ivory with gold mounting and miniatures of Count Adam Ferdinand Moltke and the Moltke arms, painted by Cornelius Høyer c. 1785. The case made in France, 1775-76.

5468. Queen Caroline Mathilde's watch, a present to the Queen from her mother-in-law, Juliane Marie. The clock case and chatelaine studded with diamonds. Made by J. F. Fistaine in Copenhagen, 1767. The works are signed: Jodin à Paris.

5470. Frederik V's collection of minerals: 86 different precious stones, semi-precious stones, minerals and artificial stones, set in individual rings, of which 25 carry the name of the stone in black letters on white enamel ground. The collection reflects the interest in the natural sciences shown during the Age of Enlightenment.

5472. Christian VII's gold rapier made by the court swordmaker, N.C. Plockross in 1766. Worn by Frederik VI at the Congress of Vienna, 1815.

5474. Cane walking stick with engraved gold knob and enamelled inscription: Quoiqu' absent toujours present: The absent one is always present. A present from Queen Marie Sophie Frederikke to Frederik VI during his participation at the Congress of Vienna.

5476. Diamond-studded rapier, a birthday present from Caroline Mathilde to Christian VII in 1769. Made by Frederik (II) Fabritius.

5478. Cane walking stick with enamelled gold knob, engraved S. May have belonged to J.F. Struensee.

5480. Rapier with gold hilt, made by Frederik (II) Fabritius, probably for Prince Frederik, the Heir Presumptive (VI) in the 1780's. Worn by Christian VIII.

5482. Queen Marie's wedding ring of gold and enamel, brilliants, and written in pearls: du 31 Juillet 1790.

5484. Medallion of gold and pearls with locks of Frederik VI's and his Queen's hair. Belonged to their daughter, Princess Caroline.

5486. Pendant of gold filigree with a lock of Frederik VI's hair and his portrait carved out of a conch-shell. Belonged to his daughter, Duchess Vilhelmine.

5488. Bracelet of gold with various semi-precious stones (The Vesuvius Stones). Sent home from Italy in 1828 by Frederik VII to his fiancée, Princess Vilhelmine.

5490. Gold medal with Frederik VI's portrait in profile, struck on the occasion of the King's death, 3.12.1839. Signed: C. Christensen.

5492. Pearl pendant in the form of a rabbit. Given to Queen Caroline Amalie in Italy 1821 by Thorvaldsen's friend, Count G.B. Sommariva.

5494. Diadem of gold, engraved and set with eleven antique cameos, acquired during Christian VIII's travels in Italy, c. 1820. Belonged to Caroline Amalie.

5496. Bracelet of gold with portrait cameo of Christian VIII, under which is a lock of hair. Cameo signed: Petrini. Pendant to no. 5494?

5498. Bracelet of gold with inlaid medal of Christian VIII and Caroline Mathilde, struck on the occasion of the anointing, 28.6.1840. Bracelet made by court jeweller Emil Ferdinand Dahl. Medal signed: C. Christensen. Belonged to Caroline Amalie.

5500. Gold medal with Christian VIII's portrait in profile, struck on the occasion of his accession, 3.12.1839. Signed: F. Krohn.

5501. Gold snuffbox with enamel and brilliants. Given as a gift at Christian VIII's anointing in 1840? Made by C.M. Weisshaupt?

5502. Caroline Amalie, miniature portrait, in crowned, diamond studded frame, to be worn as a decoration. Painted by N.C. Hansen after the painting by H. C. Jensen, and presented to Dorothea Rosen, Lady-in-Waiting, in 1869.

5504. Cylindrical watch in gold locket with portrait of Christian VIII, enamelled. Locket marked: G. Loup. Works: Elffroth & Co.

5508. Frederik VII's monogram in diamonds, presented by the King in 1851 to Madame Cathrine Christiansen in Flensborg for her services in tending the wounded in the war of 1848-50.

5510. Gold box. On the lid a double crowned FA, signifying Prince Frederik August of Nør. Made in Copenhagen in 1851 by F.W. Knoblich.

5512. Snake brooch of enamelled gold with precious stones and pendant watch. Belonged to Countess Danner.

5514. Snuffbox of gold with enamel, brilliants and Frederik VII's portrait in profile. Signed E. Young.

5516. Gold ring with Frederik VII's crowned monogram in diamonds on blue enamel with a wreath of brilliants. Made by Peter Hertz. Presented by Frederik VII on his deathbed on 15.11.1863 to the Steward of Glücksborg Castle.

5518. Handle of a riding whip, of coral and gold, made by the court jeweller J. Diderichsen, 1859.

5520. The Tunisian Order of Nishan ed-Dem, with diamonds, presented to Frederik VII in 1861.

5522. Skater in gold and Baroque pearl, made by the court jeweller J. Diderichsen in 1862 for Frederik VII, who died, however, before he received it.

5524. Jewellery set of gold with citrines, amthysts, pearls and diamonds. Belonged to Countess Danner, possibly a birthday present from Frederik VII, 1860. Made by court jeweller J. Diderichsen.

5526. Opera glasses with mother-of-pearl and enamelled gold mounting depicting Countess Danner's crowned monogram and coat-of-arms, and miniatures of the Palaces of Frederiksborg and Fredensborg. A present from Carl XV as a memento of his visit to Denmark in 1862. Supplied by Benjamin Leja in Stockholm. Made in France?

Collection of crown jewels for the use of the reigning Queen, founded by Queen Sophie Magdalene in her Will of 1746, and subsequently added to by gifts from later queens and princesses. At the last Absolutist anointing in 1840, Queen Caroline Amalie had the main part of the crown jewels remade into four sets:

5528. Set of emeralds and brilliants with diadem, necklace, brooch and earrings. Made in 1840 by C. M. Weisshaupt. The emeralds were originally a present from Christian VI to Sophie Magdalene at Frederik V's birth in 1723.

5530. Costume jewellery: eleven hearts of silver with rubies. From the 17th century.

5532. Set of pearls, rubies and diamonds with necklace, brooch and earrings. Made in 1840 by C.M. Weisshaupt. The pearl necklace belonged to Christian V's consort, Charlotte Amalie; the clasp and the two ruby-studded extra links date from 1840.

5534. The Sceptre, of gold with enamel and table-cut diamonds. Made for the coronation of Frederik III in 1648 by an unknown goldsmith in Copenhagen. Used at anointings during the period of Absolutism from Christian V in 1671 to Christian VIII in 1840.

5536. The Orb, of gold with enamel and table-cut diamonds. Made for Frederik III's coronation in 1648 in Hamburg. Used at anointings during the period of Absolutism.

5538. The Ampulla of gold with enamel and table-cut diamonds. Made for the coronation of Frederik III in 1648 by an unknown goldsmith in Copenhagen. Used at anointings during the period of Absolutism.

5540. The Anointing Rapier, of gold with enamel, table-cut and rose-cut stones. Used by the Absolutist kings and possibly by Frederik III. Originally a wedding present from Christian IV to Frederik III in 1643. Hilt of the rapier and chape of the scabbard made by the goldsmith Lucas Schaller in Hamburg. The enamelled coats-of-arms of the provinces were made for Christian V's anointing in 1671.

5542. The Amethyst for the Anointing Chair (in the Long Hall, no. 2137), in a casing with Christian V's name in gold on enamel, possibly made by Paul Kurtz, 1671. The jewel was only used when the kings sat enthroned, being otherwise replaced by an imitation. The Amethyst was used as a decoration on Frederik III's riding trappings during the coronation in 1648.

5544. The Star of the Order of the Elephant in gold and silver embroidery with pearls and table-cut stones. Made for Christian V's anointing robes in 1671.

5546. The Chain of the Order of the Elephant with Insignia, of gold with enamel and table-cut stones. The chain was made after the new statutes for the Order in 1693; the letter on the elephant's cloth signifies Dacia (Denmark). Made in Copenhagen by the goldsmith Jean Henri de Moor? The elephant possibly made by Paul Kurtz, 1671.

5548. The Chain of the Order of Dannebrog with Insignia, of gold with enamel and table-cut stones. The Chain was made after the new statutes for the Order in 1693. The letter W stands for Valdemar II Sejr, who, legend has it, received the Dannebrog from heaven during the battle of Lyndanisse in 1219. C5 signifies Christian V, who re-established the Order in 1671. The Insignia was possibly made by Paul Kurtz, 1671.

5550. Star of the Order of the Elephant, to be worn on the doublet of the Anointing Dress. Brilliants on gold and enamel. Made for Christian VI by Frederik (I) Fabritius in 1731.

5552. The star of the Order of the Elephant, of brilliants and pearls on gold and enamel. Made c. 1770 by J.F. Fistaine?

5554. Star of the Order of Dannebrog, of gold with brilliants and rubies. Made after amendments to the statutes of the Order in 1808, probably for Frederik VI.

5556. Swordbelt belonging to the Anointing Dress. Gold embroidery made for the anointing of Christian VIII in 1840 by Eug. Beauvais in Paris. The jewels of gold with enamel and diamonds belonged originally to Christian V's Swordbelt.

5558. Garters belonging to the Anointing Dress, made, like the Sword belt, in Paris in 1840. Buckles and jewels made by Frederik (I) Fabritius in 1731.
Crown Jewels for the use of the Reigning Queen:

5560. Set of brilliants consisting of necklace with seven pendants, brooch in the form of a floral bouquet, and earrings. Made in 1840 by C.M. Weisshaupt. The largest pendant in the necklace belonged to Queen Sophie Magdalene, the six smaller ones to Queen Caroline Mathilde. The two drop-earrings belonged to Queen Juliane Marie.

5562. Costume brooches: 14 bouquets of rose-cut diamonds. Belonged to Princess Charlotte Amalie.

5564. Set of rose-cut diamonds with belt and brooch to divide into 4 smaller brooches, and two necklaces. Matching pointed diamond with clasp? Made in 1840 by C.M. Weisshaupt. The stones belonged to Christian VI's sister, Princess Charlotte Amalie.

5566. Hair ornament in the form of a half-moon with brilliants and feathers of pearls. Made for Frederik VI's consort Marie c. 1810, probably by Frederik (II) Fabritius or F.V. Henriques.

5568. Pin with brilliant. Belonged to Queen Marie.

5570. String of freshwater pearls and gold locket with brilliants, within which a miniature of Christian VIII, signed: J. Møller 1840. On the back a plait of hair. Belonged to Queen Caroline Amalie.

5572. Patch of gold, enamelled, with pearls and brilliants and Christian VII's crowned mirror monogram. Belonged to Frederik VI's daughter, Crown Princess Caroline.

5592. The Crown of the Absolute Monarchs, used by the kings from Christian V to Christian VIII. Made by Paul Kurtz in Copenhagen 1670-71. Gold with enamel and table-cut stones. On the circlet 2 sapphires and 2 spinel rubies; on the cross a red sapphire. The precious stones are presumably reused from older jewels. The »large rare sapphire« on the front of the crown dates back to Frederik I and was presumably a gift to his father, Christian I, from the Duke of Milan in 1474. On the palmette above this is a table-cut diamond, behind which Christian V's monogram in gold thread can be seen. Since the abolition of Absolutism, the crown has been used at the *castrum doloris* of the deceased Kings.

5594. The Queen's Crown, made for Queen Sophie Magdalene by court jeweller Frederik (I) Fabritius in 1731. The table-cut stones are believed to have come from Queen Sophie Amalie's crown from 1648.

5596. Christian V's coronation in the chapel of Frederiksborg Palace in 1671. Sketch for an engraving, painted by Michael van Haven.

5598. Crowns and coronets of royalty and the peerage, arranged in order of precedence in 1671, during the Absolutist period.

The Arms Collection in Room 7

2801. Cross-bow, stock of walnut inlaid with engraved horn plates, showing hunting-figures, c. 1650. The cross-bow, originally a military weapon, was at this time used for hunting. – *2802.* Pair of wheel-lock pistols marked on the pommel with a crowned »G« for Ulrich Friderich Guldenlöw, c. 1665. – *2803.* War hammer. From the effects of King Christian V, c. 1575. – *2804.* Imitation Renaissance rapier, c. 1850 – *2805.* Hunting sword With King Frederik II's crowned monogram and »1585«. (cf. nos. *2806, 2811* and *2812*). – *2806.* Hunting sword, dated 1586 (cf. no. *2805*). – *2807.* Musket-rest with rapier blade and halberd; the arms of Denmark and Pomerania and the year »1590«. – *2808.* Cross-bow. On the cheek plate a crowned »C5«; butt-plate of silver with inscription: Juhst Høg Anno 1...; Denmark c. 1670. – *2809.* Two cranequins, Germany c. 1575. – *2810.* Two wheel-lock keys; possibly Copenhagen. c. 1855 and 1838. – *2811.* Rapier. With King Frederik II's monogram and motto MHZGA (Mein Hoffnung Zu Gott Allein) and the year 1584. (Cf. no. *2805*). – *2812.* Hunting knife, 1585. (Cf. no. *2805*). – *2813.* Scottish child's sword and broadsword, c. 1825. – *2814.* Cross-bow, probably Denmark c. 1650. – *2815.* Sword-hanger, gold-embroidered. 1600-1650. – *2817.* Pair of wheel-lock pistols. Marked on the barrel with the mark of Reinert Pasquier at Elsinore and the date 1623. On the stock the monogram of Christian, the Prince Elect. – *2818.* Pair of wheel-lock pistols. The pipes stamped with a crowned »C«, probably signifying Crown Prince Christian (V). Denmark (Paul Nielsen Norman?) c. 1685. – *2819.* Wheel-lock gun. The barrel stamped »C.L.« and the year »1596«. The silver butt-plate bears the name of Count Hieronymus Schlick. Coronation present for Christian IV. Saxony, 1596. – *2820.* Flint-lock rifle. The lock signed by Paul Nielsen Norman. Copenhagen c. 1670-75. -*2822.* Powder horn, redecorated with Christian IV's monogram etc. Dutch c. 1660. From Frederik VII's collection. – *2823.* Ornamented bull's horn, probably late 17th century. – *2825.* Wheel-lock rifle. The barrel stamped with a crowned »C« (cf. no. *2818*). Denmark c. 1665. – *2828.* Spurs of gilded iron. – *2829.* Pair of stirrups and curb bit for »Kranich«, Duke Anthon Günther of Oldenborg's horse (cf. the painting in the window). – *2830.* Flintlock rifle signed: Valentin Marr Copenhagen. On the butt-plate crowned »C6«. Copenhagen, 1742. – *2831.* Flint-lock rifle with inscriptions commemorating Christian V's travels in Norway in 1685. Executed by Lars Berrig in Trondheim. – *2832.* Pair of wheel-lock rifles (Polish?). On the rest-plate crowned »F3« and »1655«. – *2833.* Wheel-lock rifle. On the barrel, the name of the owner, O. Bielcke. The stock signed: Gerdt Henniges Anno 1652. – *2837.* Silver baton of King Frederik III. – *2840.* Frederik III's rapier with the King's monogram inlaid in silver on the pommel. On the blade: Peter Munich, Solingen. – *2841.* Pair of flint-lock short rifles. The lock signed: Friderich Ostermann Copenhagen. On the butt-plate the monogram of Frederik IV. Copenhagen, 1715. – *2842*. Wheel-lock gun with a crowned »C5« for Christian, the Prince Elect. The barrel stamped by Søren Rasmussen, Ålborg, 1635. – *2843*. Flint-lock rifle signed by Valentin Marr, Copenhagen. On the butt-plate Christian VI's monogram. Copenhagen 1745. – *2844*. Two pairs of gilded iron spurs. – *2845*. Wheel-lock gun. On the stock, the crowned monogram of Frederik II. Saxony c. 1585. – *2846*. Wheel-lock rifle. The stock signed »HK« (Hans Kaluga?) and »1632«. Teschen. – *2847*. Wheel-lock magazine rifle. The barrel signed: Peter Kalthoff. Anno 1646 D: 28 May Fecitt. Flensb.; and with Frederik III's monogram. – *2848*. Flintlock musketon, the lock signed: Thuraine a Paris. Used by Christian V in the Scanian war 1675-79. – *2849*. Flint-lock rifle with dog lock, signed: Heinrich Kappell. Copenhagen c. 1690-95. – *2850*. Short flint-lock rifle. The barrel and lock signed by Lorenz Helbe, Strassburg. c. 1660. – *2851*. Wheel-lock rifle (one of two, see no. *2819*). – *2852*. Wheel-lock rifle. The barrel signed by Max Wenger. On the stock, a crowned »F«, presumably for King Frederik III as Prince. Spectacle lens. – *2853*. Wheel-lock rifle; signed: Gerdt Henniges Anno 1652. On the barrel, the owner's name, O. Bielke. Germany. – *2854*. Flint-lock gun; the lock signed by Jan Knoop, Utrecht. On the barrel, the owner's name O. Bielke. Holland c. 1660. – *2855*. Flint-lock rifle, the lock signed: Lars Berrig Trundheim. On the stock, inscriptions about Christian V's travels in Norway in 1685. – *2856*. Flint-lock, short rifle (one of two, see no. *2850*). Made by H. Kappell to replace a gun lost in the battle of Lund in 1676. – *2857*. Pair of flint-lock pistols, the barrels signed: Lazarino Cominazzo. The stock carved with a back-to-back »C« (Christian V as Crown Prince). Probably by Paul Nielsen Norman. Denmark, c. 1665. – *2858*. Pair of flint-lock pistols, the locks signed: I. des Granges a Paris. On the thumb plate, a crowned »F3«. Paris c. 1670. – *2859*. Pair of flint-lock pistols, the locks signed: Thuraine a Paris. On the butt, a crowned »C« signifying Christian V as Crown Prince. Paris c. 1670. – *2860*. Pair of flintlock pistols, the locks signed: Friderich Ostermann Copenhagen. On the lock, the crowned monogram of Christian V. Copenhagen c. 1685. – *2861*. Dress rapier with Hercules hilt of silver. The blade signed: Johannes Tesche me fecit Solingen. Germany, c. 1650. – *2862*. So-called Oldenborg rapier with hilt covered with chased silver. Dated 1576. Northern Germany. – *2863*. Anthon Günther's rapier (cf. no. *2829*). The blade signed: Clemens Horn me fecit Solingen. Germany or the Netherlands c,1620-30. – *2864*. Gustavus II Adolphus's rapier. The blade stamped by Johann Tesche, Solingen. Netherlands c. 1620-1630. – *2865*. Dress rapier with lion hilt. The blade stamped by Johannes Wunders, Solingen. Germany c. 1650. – *2866*. Hunting sword with carved hilt of rhinoceros-horn formed as a group of animals by J.M. Maucher. Germany, c. 1650. – *2867*. Rapier with chiselled steel hilt, on the blade (Solingen), engraved portraits of princes, etc., from the time of the Thirty Years' War. Probably Germany, c. 1640. – *2868*. King Christian V's rapier worn in the Scanian war 1675-79. The blade signed: Tomas de Aiala, Toledo. c. 1675. – *2869*. Hunting sword with grip of agate; mountings decorated with enamel and cut stones. c. 1675. – *2870*. Hunting sword with gilt grip set with half pearls. Probably Germany, c. 1720. - 2871. Hunting sword, made to match no. *2870*. The blade signed »ZZ« and »Ziegler«. Belonged to Frederik IV's brother Carl. – *2872*. King Frederik IV's rapier with grip of agate, bent at the explosion of a gun in the foundry, 1729, endangering the King. Probably Danish, c. 1720. – *2873*. Pair of wheel-lock pistols, the lock signed »FP« (Francois Poumerol, Paris?). On the ramrods, the ciphers of King Christian IV and his Queen. – *2874*. Pair of flint-lock pistols, the stocks of ivory. The locks signed: De la Haye Maestricht. Netherlands, c. 1675. King Frederik IV's cipher later added to the thumb plate. – *2875*. Pair of flint-lock pistols, the locks signed: V. Marr Cop.h.gen. Lock and barrel plated with gold. On the butt-plate the crowned monogram of Frederik V. Executed 1766. – *2876*. Flint-lock child's gun, the lock signed: Friderich Ostermann Copenhagen. On the thumb-plate, crowned »F4«. Copenhagen, 1700. – *2877*. Flint-lock child's gun, the lock signed: Friderich Ostermann Copenhagen. On the thumb-plate, back-to-back crowned »C« (Christian VI as Crown Prince). Copenhagen, c. 1710. – *2878*. Two flint-lock guns, the locks signed: V. Marr A Copenh. On the thumb-plates resp. ciphers of Christian VI and his Queen. Silver mounting marked »1742« by Jens Pedersen Komløv. – *2879*. Flint-lock child's rifle, signed on the lock: Valentin Marr Copenhagen. On the butt-plate, crowned back-to-back »F« for Crown Prince Frederik (V). Copenhagen c. 1735-40. – *2880*. Flint-lock gun, the lock signed: Valentin Marr Copenhagen. Owner's mark like no. *2879*. Copenhagen 1745. – *2881*. Flint-lock gun, the lock signed: Valentin Marr A Copenhagen. On the barrel, Marr's stamp-group. Copenhagen, c. 1751. – *2882*. Flint-lock rifle, the lock signed: Johan Winter. On the thumb-plate, Frederik IV's crowned cipher. Copenhagen c. 1720. – *2883*. Flint-lock rifle, the butt-plate signed: I.M. Hoffmann a Suhl 1709. The lock signed by A. Gebauer. Copenhagen c. 1730. – *2884*. Double-barrelled gun, the lock signed: Valentin Marr A Copenhagen. On the butt-plate the cipher of Crown Prince Prince Frederik (V). Copenhagen c. 1740. – *2885*. Flint-lock gun, the barrel stamped with Marr's stamp-group. The lock signed: Valentin Marr A Copenhagen. On the butt-plate, Frederik V's crowned cipher. Copenhagen, 1751. – *2886*. Flint-lock gun, the lock signed: Valentin Marr A Copenhagen. On the butt-plate Christian VII's crowned cipher. Copenhagen, 1751. – *2887*. Pair of flint-lock pistols, the locks signed: V.

Marr A Copenhagen. On the thumb-plate, Christian VI's crowned cipher. Mountings of mother-of-pearl. Copenhagen, 1733. – *2888.* Pair of flint-lock pistols. The locks signed: A: Gebauer Copenhagen. On the thumb-plate, Christian VI's crowned cipher. Copenhagen, 1734. – *2889.* Pair of flint-lock pistols. The lock signed: Heinrich Jahn: A Wernige Roda. Germany, 1735. Probably belonged to Christian VI. – *2890.* Pair of flint-lock pistols, the barrel signed: Jacob Kuchenreuter. Frederik VI's target pistols. Regensburg, 1740. – *2891.* Pair of flint-lock pistols. The lock signed: L. Marr Kiøbenhavn. On the pommel boss, the cipher of Crown Prince Frederik (VI), Copenhagen, c. 1785.

The Commandant's Residence

The original commandant's residence lies with its facade facing Øster Voldgade; it was erected in 1760-63 by the architect Jacob Fortling, and, until 1972, it was occupied by the Curator of the Rosenborg Collection.

The ground floor of the building houses the collection of Royal costumes. Two rooms facing the garden are used for *changing exhibitions* of the exhibits belonging to the main collection, presented here according to exhibition principles that cannot be practised in Christian IV's old palace.

List of artists and craftsmen

Bibliography

Otto Andrup: Den kongelige Samling paa Rosenborg gennem hundrede aar. I. Den chronologiske Samling. (Kbh. 1933)

Mogens Bencard (& G.A. Markova): Christian 4.s Pragtsølv. Christian IV's Royal Plate. (Kbh. 1988)

Mogens Bencard & Jørgen Hein: De danske Kongers Kronologiske Samling. The Royal Danish Collections. Les Collections des Rois de Danemark. Die Sammlungen der Dänischen Könige. (Kbh. 1989)

Gudmund Boesen: Christian den Femtes Rosenborgtapeter fra den skaanske Krig. (English summary). (Kbh. 1949)

Venetianske Glas på Rosenborg. I vetri veneziani del Castello di Rosenborg. Venetian glass at Rosenborg Castle. (Kbh. 1960)

Danmarks Riges Regalier. (English summary). (Kbh. 1986)

P. Brock: Historiske Efterretninger om Rosenborg. (Kbh. 1881-83)

Sigrid Flamand Christensen: Kongedragterne fra 17. og 18. Aarhundrede. Bd. I-II. (English summary; deutsche Zusammenfassung). (Kbh. 1940)

Arne Hoff, H.D. Schepelern & Gudmund Boesen: Royal Arms at Rosenborg. Vol. I-II. (Kbh. 1956)

H.C. Bering Liisberg: Rosenborg og Lysthusene i Kongens Have. (Kbh. 1914)

Preben Mellbye-Hansen: De danske Kronjuveler. (Kbh. 1990)

Åshild Paulsen: Magnus Berg. (English summary). (Oslo 1989)

Friedrich Spuhler, Preben Mellbye-Hansen, Majken Thorvildsen & Mogens Bencard (red.): De Danske Kroningstæpper. Denmark's Coronation Carpets. (Kbh. 1987)

Vilhelm Wanscher: Rosenborgs Historie 1606-1634. (Kbh. 1930)

J.J.A. Worsaae: Optegnelser om Rosenborg-Samlingen i 25 Aar, 1858-1883. (Kbh. 1886)

Catalogues of special exhibitions

Mogens Bencard: Wolffgang Heimbach. 1980
Jørgen Hein: Børn på Rosenborg. 1981
Jørgen Hein: Kongelig Porcelæn på Rosenborg. 1982
Mogens Bencard: Maria Sibylla Merian. 1983
Jørgen Hein: Venetianske Glas. 1984
Ole Thamdrup & Katia Johansen: Europas Svigerfar. Fotografier fra Christian IX's regeringstid. 1985
Mogens Bencard: Kongens København. Bybilleder 1640-1860. 1986
Jørgen Hein & Katia Johansen: Sophie Amalie – den onde dronning? 1986
Mogens Bencard: Robert og Rosenborg. 1987
Jørgen Hein, Mogens Bencard, Katia Johansen & Preben Mellbye-Hansen: Christian IV's Skatte. Christian IV's Treasures. I Steffen Heiberg (red.): Christian IV og Europa. Christian IV and Europe. The 19th Council of Europe Exhibition 1988.
Åshild Paulsen: Magnus Berg 1666-1739. Elfenben. 1989
Katia Johansen: Kongelige Kjoler / Royal Gowns. 1990
Mogens Bencard: Sølvmøbler / Silver Furniture. 1992
Kongen i Norge. 1992
Katia Johansen: Kongeblåt på Rosenborg. 1993
Mogens Bencard og Kirsten Aschengreen Piacenti: Royal Treasures from Denmark. 1709: Frederik IV in Florence. 1994

Selected articles after 1980

Mogens Bencard:
The Royal Danish Collections at Rosenborg. Journal of Museum Management and Curatorship, 3,3,1984.
A note on the Rosenborg Collection in Copenhagen.

Oliver Impey & Arthur Mac Gregor: The Origins of Museums. Oxford 1985.

Service de toilette de la duchesse Hedvig Sofia. Versailles à Stockholm. Nationalmuseum. Stockholm 1985.

Bernstein aus der dänischen Kunstkammer. Kunst & Antiquitäten, VI, 1987.

Two 17th century Eskimos at Rosenborg Palace. Man & Society, 12, 1989.

Denmark's Castle of Roses. The Interior, Sept., 1990.

The Glass Cabinet at Rosenborg Palace. Gottfried Fuch's arrangement of 1714 rediscovered. Journal of the History of Collections, 3,1,1991.

Rosenborg Palace. The Royal Danish Collections. Living Architecture, 11,1992.

Eine private fürstliche Kunstkammer: Rosenborg 1718 / Gottorf 1694, in: Andreas Grote (ed.): Macrocosmos in Microcosmo. Die Welt in der Stube. Zur Geschichte des Sammelns 1450-1800. Opladen 1994.

Mogens Bencard & Jørgen Hein:
Three Cabinets on Stands from the Seventeenth Century. Furniture History. XXI, 1985.

Jørgen Hein:
Das Glaskabinett in Schloss Rosenborg. Kunst & Antiquitäten, IV, 1984.

Bergkristall und Halbedelsteinen des Grünen Kabinetts. Kunst & Antiquitäten, II, 1985.

Goldemail des Manierismus & Frühbarock. Kunst & Antiquitäten, II, 1988.

Christian IV and the Goldsmiths. The Apollo, August, 1988.

Der dänische Krönungsdegen. Kunst & Antiquitäten, IV, 1989.

Reassembled Venetian Glasses from the Glass Room at Rosenborg Palace. Journal of Glass Studies, 31, 1989.

Ivories by Gottfried Wolffram. The Scandinavian Journal of Design History, 1, 1990.

Löwe und Schwan. Der dänische »Krönungspokal«. Kunst & Antiquitäten, IX, 1991.

Venetian or Saxon: Early Saxon Glass in the Glass Room at Rosenborg Palace. Journal of Glass Studies, 34, 1991.

Fashionable Flower Enamels. Vibeke Woldbye (ed.): Flowers into Art. The Hague 1991.

Splendour in Defeat. Danish Court Jewelry by Paul Kurtz and his workshop, in: The Scandinavian Journal of Design History, 4, 1994.

Das grüne Kabinett im Schloss Rosenborg – Schatzkammer oder Raritäten-Kabinett, in: Andreas Grote (ed.): Macrocosmos in Microcosmo. Die Welt als Stube. Zur Geschichte des Sammelns 1450 bis 1800, Opladen 1994.

Jørgen Wadum:
The Winter Room at Rosenborg Castle. The Apollo, August, 1988.